Introduction

Until recently, the teaching of design and technology in the primary school was rare. Good practice was found in some schools but, in many, craft, model-making and, occasionally, problem-solving exercises in science were the only contributions to design and technology. Now the National Curriculum makes design and technology a foundation subject of the school curriculum.

In science the aim is to understand, explain and investigate our environment. In design and technology the aim is to solve problems, by making use of and controlling materials and phenomena. On the surface, science is the *why* and technology is the *how*. In practice, the distinction between science and technology is not as clear as this. It is often blurred, like the distinction between art and design.

The essence of design and technology is the application of skills and knowledge to solve problems which arise from the needs of people and societies. In the classroom, teachers must give children real problems. These might arise spontaneously or be contrived or planned to fit in with topics or themes.

For example, suppose the cupboard door will not stay open; we could take the opportunity to ask the children how to fix it. On another occasion, the children trip over a doormat; we ask them to think of ways to prevent this. If the children are involved in a topic on the Romans, then they could be asked to design and make a siege weapon, planning the design and technology to fit in with the existing work.

WHY INCLUDE DESIGN AND TECHNOLOGY ?

In the primary school design and technology may:
- bring relevance to pupils' learning and enhance motivation;
- make abstract concepts (like force and energy) more meaningful;
- highlight considerations, such as economics and aesthetics, which enter into product design;
- increase awareness of and competence in an increasingly technological society;
- foster creativity and disciplined imagination;
- encourage logical thinking and problem-solving skills and strategies;
- provide opportunities to reduce role distinctions between boys and girls.

Design and Technology – concepts and aims

Design and technology is sometimes defined as the skills, processes and knowledge used to produce a needed artefact, system or device. Children of any age or ability can respond at their own level to the challenge of 'Can you make a . . .?'. What they need is motivation and success.

When thinking about design and technology, three aspects need to be considered: products, processes and people.

Products

Knowledge, understanding, concepts and ideas about:

- materials and components eg sources, cost, properties, limitations.
- structures, eg static and mobile.
- forces eg cause and effects.
- energy eg sources, forms, conversion, transmission, cost.
- movement eg in a straight line, in a curve, rotation.
- systems eg organizing collections of components which interact to make a product.
- control (including Information Technology) eg changing and controlling the man-made environment.

Processes

Mental, physical and social skills associated with:

- recognizing that there is a need or a problem;
- generating ideas for solutions;
- researching and producing a design brief;
- developing the most appropriate solution;
- producing the solution;
- appraising the solution.

People

Personal, social, cultural and historical aspects:

- the needs of individuals and of groups in society, giving rise to demand to be supplied by the design and technology process;
- the need to consider the aesthetics of the product;
- the consideration of human factors (ergonomics) like body size and shape, comfort, fatigue and human psychology.
- the use of design and technology to care for and control the environment to make it habitable and pleasant to live in.

It is useful to think of design and technology as a collection of stages, which may be depicted in a number of ways. We have found our model – shown on page 109, useful to the primary teacher for planning design and technology activities and also for children themselves to use as a guide or structure.

The National Curriculum and Design and Technology

The National Curriculum for Technology identifies five attainment targets (ATs):

AT 1: Identifying needs and opportunities

'Pupils should be able to identify and state clearly needs and opportunities for design and technological activities' as they might arise at home, at school, at work, in the community and in leisure pursuits.

AT 2: Generating a design proposal

Pupils should be able to produce a description of the characteristics of what is needed 'and develop it into a realistic, appropriate and achievable design'.

AT 3: Planning and making

'Pupils should be able to prepare a plan to achieve their design and to identify, manage and use appropriate resources', mental and physical, and make 'artefacts (objects made by people), systems (sets of objects or activities which perform a task) and environments (surroundings made or developed by people)'.

AT 4: Evaluating

Pupils should be able to appraise what they and others have created in their design and technological activities and 'communicate and act upon' that appraisal.

AT 5: Information technology

'Pupils should be able to use IT to communicate and handle information, design, develop and evaluate models, take measurements and control movement.'

Attainment targets 1 to 4 combine to give Profile Component 1 (Design and Technology Capability). The fifth Attainment Target is treated separately to give Profile Component 2 (Information Technology Capability).

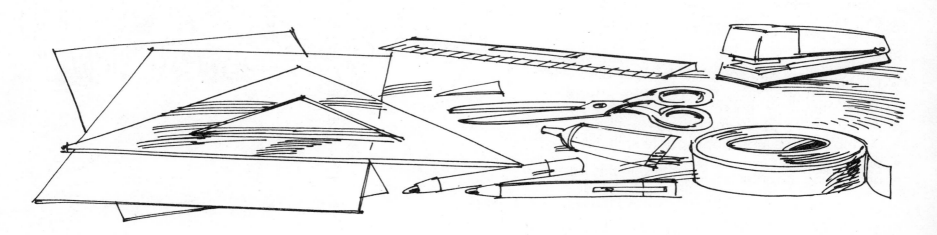

These attainment targets constitute the skills and processes, knowledge and understanding which pupils of different abilities and maturities are expected to have by the end of each Key Stage. What exactly is 'to be taught' is described in the Programmes of Study for each attainment target. The Programmes of Study have two components: some activities are suggested which pupils at particular levels should experience in order to develop a particular capability at that level, and some content is suggested that should be taught in order to achieve a particular level across all the attainment targets. This content can be divided into products (concepts, ideas, facts, experiences), processes (skills) and people (personal, social, cultural and economic aspects).

Products
- materials and components
- energy
- systems
- structures
- mechanisms.

Processes
- exploring and investigating
- imaging and generating
- modelling and communicating
- organizing and planning
- making
- appraising
- using tools and equipment.

People
- business and economics
- aesthetics
- health and safety
- social and environmental aspects.

Links with the National Curriculum for Science, Mathematics and English are also in the Technology document.

The tasks and activities described in this book, and the skills, processes, knowledge and attitudes encouraged through these tasks reflect the requirements of the National Curriculum for Technology.

Information Technology

Information Technology often plays a significant part in professional design and technology, business, commerce and industry. Large amounts of data from surveys are stored and processed by computer in market research; outline proposals and estimates may be stored on a computer disc for fast access, easy modification and high-quality presentation; computer-aided design packages show what some device will look like and allow for modification before it goes to the expensive prototype stage. In the design of a microchip, for instance, the computer takes an even bigger role in replicating circuits, matching modules and checking that the chip functions as intended in a fraction of the time it would take a team of designers.

At the production stage, computer control of plant and machine is well-known from the publicity given to it by the car industry. Aircraft and cars use electronic systems to display information and control some of the functions, just as the automatic washing machine does. Even the supermarket check-out communicates with a stock-keeping computer as the bar codes on goods pass over the laser reader. One aim of design and technology education is to introduce children to the role and potential of Information Technology in design and technology and to develop a willingness to use Information Technology at an appropriate level in their work.

Opportunities to develop Information Technology capability in schools will vary according to the resources and equipment available. The range of quality software for use by primary children is increasing. Much of it can be used at different levels throughout the school and is not class/age specific.

Choosing software

When choosing and using software packages, consider whether the packages offer one or more of the following:

- Structured reinforcement of skills, knowledge and understanding, for example
  Mathematics: *Trains, Shopping, Beat the Clock* or *Angle Turner*.
  Language: *Starspell, Brickup, Anagram* or *Handwriting*.

- Opportunities to use and develop problem solving and thinking skills, for example
  Mathematics: *Crash, Watchperson* or *Boxes*.
  Language: *Thinklinks* or *Animal, Vegetable, Mineral*.
  Science: *Kingdom* or *Measure and Tell*.
  Design: *Build, Doodle* or *Hunt*.

- Games and simulations (usually cross-curricular), for example
  Mathematics: *Connect 4* or *Halving*.
  Language: *Flowers of Crystal* or *Granny's Garden*.
  Science: *Understanding Weather, Gliders* or *Microbug*.
  History: *Mary Rose* or *Unearthing the Past*.

- Data handling, storage, retrieval and interpretation, for example
  Mathematics: *My Mathematical Self* or *Eureka*.
  Language: *Factfile, Folio* or *Storyline*.
  Science: *Quest, Weatherstation* or *Identify*.

Some software packages are designed to encourage control capabilities, for example, Logo-based computer programs like *Dart*. The BBC Buggy and Turtle operate

in a similar way. If a computer is not available, then Big Trak or LEGO Technic can be used in a similar way. Some children may already be familiar with these from home. They may also have encountered programmable calculators, spelling and word-aid devices and programmable electronic games. In music, electronic keyboards can also be introduced.

Here are some suggestions to help to develop Information Technology capability. These indicate a general progression but should not be tied too tightly to ages of children and stages of education.

Early Years (Nursery/Reception/Middle Infants)

Children should be aware that Information Technology can be used to present information in a variety of ways and that information can be stored in and retrieved from a computer.
Experiences might include:
- everyday use of the computer across the curriculum with simple games, simulations and structured reinforcement tasks;
- using calculators, especially those with a simple memory;
- using concept or overlay keyboards to construct simple sentences and short stories;
- using hand-held, electronic games, spelling and number aids and programmable toys.

Middle Years (Older Infants/Younger Juniors)

Children should be able to use Information Technology to present and change information and to use simple, commercially produced packages and databases. Experiences might include:

- storing and displaying information collected during science and mathematics investigations or environmental studies surveys;
- using simple word-processing across the curriculum to draft and produce stories, short reports and diaries;
- using simple software packages which involve interaction, data input and data retrieval;
- devising simple instructions to control the movements of devices like Big Trak, the BBC Buggy or the Turtle.

Upper Years (Middle/Older Juniors)

Children should be able to use Information Technology in a variety of ways to fulfil a need, to store and process data, to use software packages and be aware of everyday applications of Information Technology. Experiences might include:

- using software packages of various kinds and for different purposes across the curriculum;
- using databases with which they can interact to store, amend and use data collected during investigations, while on visits and when carrying out fieldwork;
- using concept keyboards or word-processing facilities to produce and print stories, reports, newsletters and publications like school magazines or concert programmes, with illustrations if possible;
- working independently with controlled devices like the BBC Buggy or LEGO Technic;
- using Logo-based computer programs like *Dart* to emulate computer-aided design by producing visual displays of artefacts or devices;

- visits to places where Information Technology is used in business, commerce or industry, for example, to a library, supermarket, office or factory.

Use whatever Information Technology is appropriate to extend the experience of your children. Page 125 onwards gives sources of information and materials relating to Information Technology.

Into the classroom

Design and technology arises in many areas of the curriculum and so it is well-suited to topic or thematic

work and cross-curricular approaches. It can help to unify skills, knowledge and understanding, and thus experiences provided in the primary school are more meaningful and relevant. Your task is to develop the opportunities for design and technology to take place and provide a flexible framework through which children can practise skills and develop expertise and understanding.

Starting points

Nursery and reception-class teachers can provide a firm foundation for design and technology through experiences with materials (like sand, water and clay) and play with equipment like blocks and construction kits. By handling a variety of materials, the children begin to understand how materials behave when treated in different ways. This knowledge can be applied, as needed, when solving problems.

Problem solving

Problem-solving strategies are called for when meeting needs. At their best, these problem-solving strategies greatly enhance interest and motivation, encourage logical thinking and offer opportunities for creativity and imagination. But being creative and imaginative cannot occur in a vacuum. Children cannot simply be sent away and told to create. They will need the necessary knowledge and skills, or the means and willingness to acquire them, in order to start. What is important is to foster independence in the design and technology process and to widen and deepen and make more challenging the tasks and activities which the children encounter.

Some problems we set children lead to particular solutions, for example 'Design and make a wheelbarrow'. These *closed* problems are quite

common in everyday life, and children can acquire some skills and competencies through them. *Open* problems are those which lend themselves to a variety of solutions.

Five children or five groups might well produce five devices or solutions, all different and yet all fulfilling the design brief, for example 'Design and make a device to start the races on sports day'. However, from the point of view of design and technology with children, there are what we call *false* problems. These are problems which, like parlour tricks, need one key – and often obscure – piece of information in order to solve them. For example, it is possible to balance six nails, each measuring 6 in, on the head of another 6-in nail.

Whether you can 'solve' this problem depends upon either an accidental discovery of the solution or knowledge of the interlocking capabilities of these nails. Unless you have taught that knowledge to the children (and, presumably, see it as worth teaching), they will simply be frustrated by the task and develop an inappropriate image of design and technology as a collection of tricks. Ingenuity does have a part to play in design and technology but this kind of task seems more likely to thwart than encourage it.

Teacher involvement

Ultimately you should aim for the children to identify needs and problems and to design and reach satisfactory solutions for themselves. Your role alters as these abilities develop.

Leader: free talk between you and pupil or group in which you guide and structure progress, perhaps by providing a design brief to follow or by leading a brainstorming session.

Questioner: you ask key questions to focus children's attention on pertinent aspects of the problem and direct observations and ideas towards possible solutions.

Assessor: you appraise the ideas, suggested design and/or final solution by questions and discussion which lead children to explain and justify what they have done.

Challenger: you ask open-ended questions or challenge children to do something, perhaps initially focusing on specific skills, materials or knowledge, and gradually widening experience.

Observer: you stand back and observe as children independently generate their own problems and solutions.

Organization and safety

If the children have not been involved in design and technology activities before, it is advisable to begin with a small group, at least until some experience has been gained. The group can work on a design and technology task while their classmates are involved in other curriculum activities. An extra pair of hands – an auxiliary or a parent – if available, can also be useful.

As with any activity or experience provided for children, safety is of paramount importance. Some simple guidelines follow but, as always, you must be the final judge of what is appropriate and safe for the class. If in doubt, always err on the side of caution.

Before beginning design and technology activities check that:
- there is plenty of working space for the children;
- unnecessary books, materials and equipment have been cleared away from the work surfaces;
- resources are easily and safely available to all the children;
- tools to be used are of good quality, in good condition and stored safely;
- the groups are adequately supervised during the work;
- protective goggles and aprons are available if needed;
- the children have been instructed in safe practices, procedures and the use of protective equipment.

During the activities safe working habits should be encouraged, for example, the safe handling of tools, calm movement around the room, a sense of responsibility towards self and others.

Finally, the task of tidying away and leaving things clean and safe should be a routine task expected of the children.

Using this book

Since design and technology involves the application of skills and knowledge to meet needs and solve problems, we have provided tasks and activities which reflect this. These tasks have been grouped into five major themes, most of which are subdivided into smaller topics.

The first chapter of activities, 'Fit and well', has the topic web Homes; 'Taking it easy' has the topic web Machines; 'Out and about' has Transport; 'Keeping in touch' has Communications and 'Free-time' has Holidays.

For each theme, there is a planning web to show the main lines of development within the primary curriculum, incorporating the topics and suggesting further links. There is also a list of possible starting-points for each theme or topic.

Tying tasks to specific age ranges is often difficult. Many briefs, or problems, can be realized or solved at different levels according to the age, ability and experience of the child, and the resources and equipment available to her. Age ranges are suggested for the tasks but they are only a guide, as are the suggested working group sizes.

For each task or activity a number of possible solutions are indicated. In most cases these are for you, not for the children. They are not intended for use as 'knitting-pattern' solutions. Accept any idea or solution from the children that is feasible and fulfils the brief. Solutions are suggested for both structural technology (ie using purchased materials like dowel, 1cm square cross section lengths of wood and prepared wheels) and 'alternative' technology (ie using boxes, string, bobbins and scraps of wood). The 'alternative' approach is open to *all* schools, since such materials are often freely available. Where money is available, a

more structural approach should be used so that the children can design and construct with more sophisticated design and technology techniques. One such structural approach is that described by Pat Williams and David Jinks in their book *Design and Technology 5–12* (Falmer Press).

The brief for many of the tasks can be given orally as the children's interest, as well as the topic itself, develops. The children themselves should be encouraged to generate some of the problems to solve. However, certain activities can be used for assessment, and these have been provided on worksheets which may be photocopied for class use (pages 108 to 123).

Some of the tasks require specific materials. In all other cases, a basic list is given of what the children need. The intention is that, where possible, they have access to *all* the design and technology resources available, to develop their creativity and stretch their imagination.

This book is meant to be a starting point in design and technology, from which more independent invention, design and realization can follow.

Fit and well

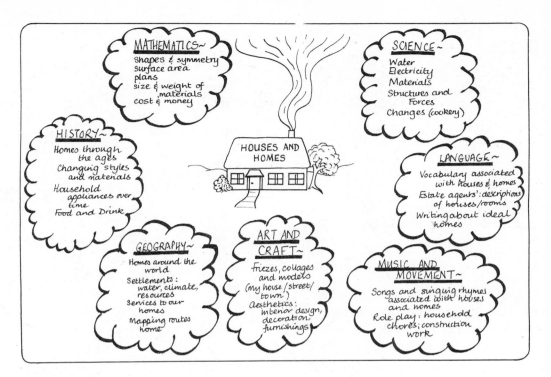

MATHEMATICS~
shapes & symmetry
surface area
plans
size & weight of
materials
cost & money

SCIENCE~
Water
Electricity
Materials
Structures and
Forces
Changes (cookery)

HISTORY~
Homes through
the ages
Changing styles
and materials
Household
appliances over
time
Food and Drink

HOUSES AND HOMES

LANGUAGE~
Vocabulary associated
with houses & homes
Estate agents': descriptions
of houses/rooms
Writing about ideal
homes

GEOGRAPHY~
Homes around the
world
Settlements:
water, climate,
resources
Services to our
homes
Mapping routes
home

ART AND CRAFT~
Friezes, collages
and models
(my house/street/
town)
Aesthetics:
interior design,
decoration,
furnishings

MUSIC AND MOVEMENT~
Songs and singing rhymes
associated with houses
and homes
Role play: household
chores; construction
work

A roof over your head

Starting points

Topics
- Houses through the ages.
- Homes around the world.
- Survival.
- Animal homes.
- Buildings.
- Strength and shape.

Visits
- Building site.
- Estate agents.
- Do-it-yourself centre.
- An historic building (eg castle or abbey).

Stories and rhymes
- *The Three Pigs* (traditional) retold by Tony Ross (Andersen Press).
- *The Hobbit* by J R R Tolkein (Chapter 1) (Unwin Paperbacks).
- *Robinson Crusoe* by Daniel Defoe (Usborne).
- *Wind in the Willows* by Kenneth Grahame (Methuen).
- *Little House on the Prairie* by L. Ingalls Wilder (Puffin).
- *The Borrowers* by Mary Norton (Puffin).
- *Strange House* by Raymond Briggs (Beaver).
- *Junk Castle* by Robin Klein (Oxford).

Events
- Accounts of people who have survived following a shipwreck or plane crash.
- Local building work.

Building a house

Age range
Four to seven.

Group size
Pairs or small groups.

What you need
Construction kits, large sheets of cardboard, large cardboard boxes, wide adhesive tape about 50 cm long.

Starting points
- Make a home corner.
- Read stories about houses eg *The House That Jack Built* by William Stobbs (Oxford University Press).
- Discuss animal homes (eg snail and shell).
- Look at a doll's house.

Task
Can you use the construction bricks to build a house for the play people to live in?

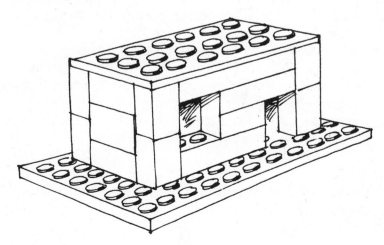

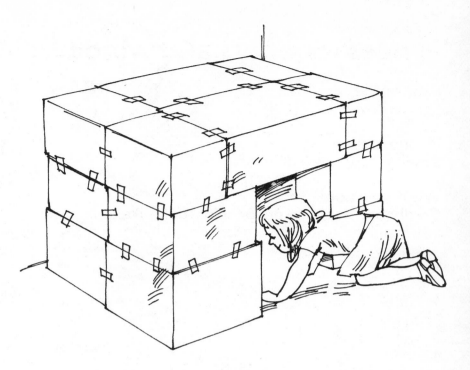

Can you use boxes to build a house into which you can crawl?

Other information
- Although small-scale models can be made by individual children, there should be an opportunity for a group of children to build a child-size version.
- By limiting the amount of adhesive tape, the children will have to decide where it is most needed and use it economically. This makes them realize that there are limits to resources and raises economic awareness.

Follow-up
Make a window in the house.
Vary the bonding patterns (link to science activities on strength of structures).

Hinges for doors and windows

Age range
Four to seven.

Group size
Small groups or whole class.

What you need
Cardboard box, scissors or snips, adhesive tape, clear polythene cut from bags, adhesive, string, paper-fasteners, fabric scraps (various weaves), vinyl fabric.

Starting points
- Look for places where hinges are used (eg door, window, toilet seat, spectacles, letterbox, caskets).
- Collect different types of hinge.
- Visit a DIY centre to look at hinges.

Task
Design and make a hinged door for the three little pigs' house, which will keep out the wolf. Can you put a hinged window in their house?

Other information
- Before beginning the task warn the children about the risks of trapping fingers in hinged structures.
- Test the solutions by blowing on the doors and windows ('huffing and puffing') or by using a hand-held fan.
- If the children use fabric hinges, they should be encouraged to consider the effect of the weave on the sag of the door or window.
- Springy material used to make hinges may also be used to make self-closing doors and windows.
- Leather was once used in this way as hinges for small objects. The earliest-known metal hinges were made from copper and were found on Tutankhamun's folding bed in his tomb, dating from 1,350 BC.

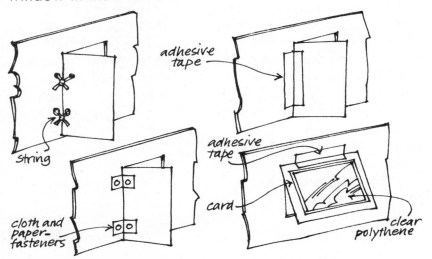

string

cloth and paper-fasteners

adhesive tape

adhesive tape

card

clear polythene

Build a two-storey house

Age range
Six to nine.

Group size
Pairs or small groups.

What you need
A4-size sheets of thick and thin card, clear polythene, small boxes (eg biscuit boxes), large boxes (eg shoe boxes), adhesive tape, string, straws, pieces of fabric, paper-fasteners, tubes (eg toilet-roll tubes), paints, brushes.

Starting points
- Visit a DIY centre.
- Visit an estate agent's office and collect descriptions of different styles of house. Observe a house being built locally.

Task
A photocopiable worksheet is available on page 110 to give to the children as a technology brief.

Other information
- The children will need to produce a design plan before they begin, which should include their costing of the materials they plan to use.
- Materials should be 'on sale' on a table in the classroom and labelled with their prices. The work could be linked to mathematics and money.
- Appraise the houses on cost, appearance and utility.

Follow-up
- Why do we paint woodwork?
- Why are plastic gutters used more than metal ones?

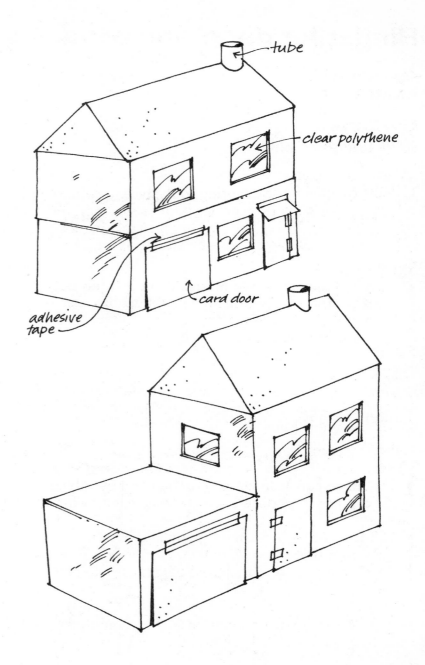

tube

clear polythene

card door

adhesive tape

Roof it!

Age range
Six to nine.

Group size
Small groups.

What you need
Offcuts of vinyl floor covering, polystyrene ceiling tiles, a large cardboard box, garden canes or wood laths, adhesive tape, string, straw, choice of fabric pieces (permeable and impermeable), stout scissors, bottles.

Starting points
- Discuss why roofs slope.
- Closely observe a selection of roofing materials.
- Collect pictures of different types of roof.
- Find a leaking roof, perhaps in the school. What causes it?

Task
Design and build a roof which does not leak.

Other information
- Provide a range of suitable and unsuitable materials.
- The large cardboard box can be used by all the children as the house base on to which the roof must rest.
- The finished object should be tested. Use a watering can to simulate rain. A sheet of sugar paper on the floor of the house can be used as a rain detector.

Follow-up
Guttering: solve the problem of water running off the roof and on to the front of the house.

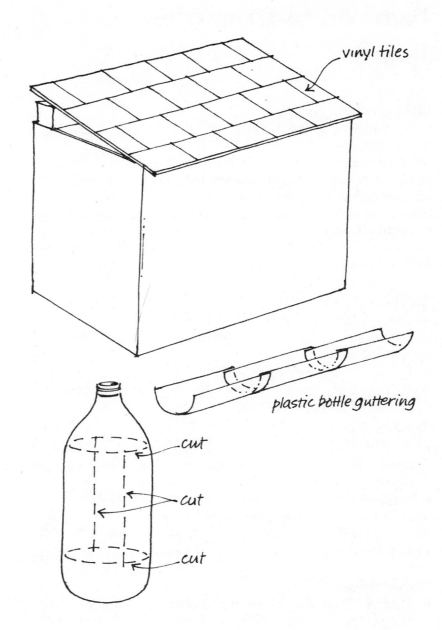

vinyl tiles

plastic bottle guttering

cut

cut

cut

Two rooms from one

Age range
Seven to eleven.

Group size
Individuals or small groups.

What you need
Large cardboard boxes; sheets of card from cereal or similar boxes; lengths of wood, 1cm^2 cross-section, eg jelutong or strips cut from stout corrugated cardboard; soundproofing materials eg cotton wool, newspaper, cloth and foil; adhesive and spreaders; adhesive tape, tools appropriate to the materials used.

Starting point
- Draw plans of the children's own homes.
- Discuss the need for an extra bedroom with the arrival of a new baby.
- Consider the function and use of rooms in a house.
- Collect descriptions of houses, with photographs, from estate agents.
- Look at plans and elevations of houses being built, available from a local building site or estate agents.

Task
Design and build a dividing wall for your house. It should split the large room into two smaller, equal-sized rooms. It should be strong and should be soundproofed in some way.

Other information
- Discuss with the children possible solutions before they begin the task. If their ideas do not fit in with the

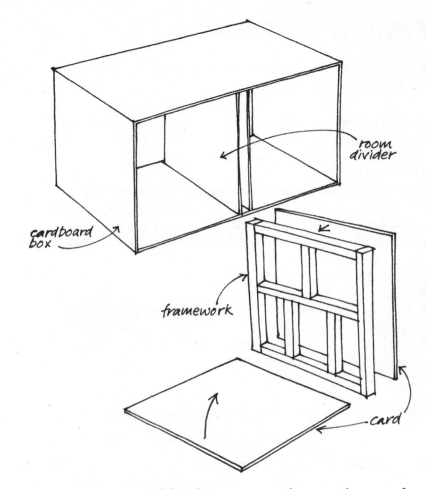

resources available, then present them with one of the possible solutions. By providing a solution now, the children can learn about the function of a strong skeleton framework. In later tasks they will be working with such structures with less guidance.
- The box house is the first stage in a sequence of activities, so a stout box is needed for each group.
- Link the task to science work on sound and soundproofing.

22

Light up the rooms

Age range
Seven to eleven.

Group size
Individuals or small groups.

What you need
Box house (see previous activity), two bulbs with bulbholders, plastic-coated copper wire, paper clips, drawing pins, Blu-tak, 1.5v battery, adhesive tape, alternative materials for switches, small screwdriver.

Starting points
- Discuss utilities in the home.
- Discuss the work of Joseph Swan or Thomas Edison.

Task
Fit a light to the ceiling of one of your rooms. Work it with a switch fixed on the wall.

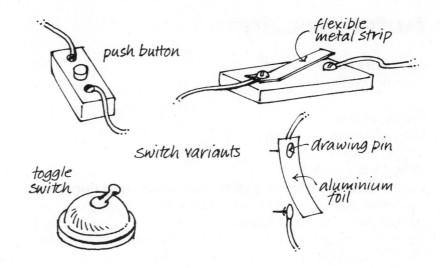

push button

flexible metal strip

switch variants

drawing pin

toggle switch

aluminium foil

Put a light in the second room so that it will operate from the same battery. Make a switch for that room, too.

Other information
- The solution for two lights shown here has the bulbs connected *in parallel* so that they work independently.

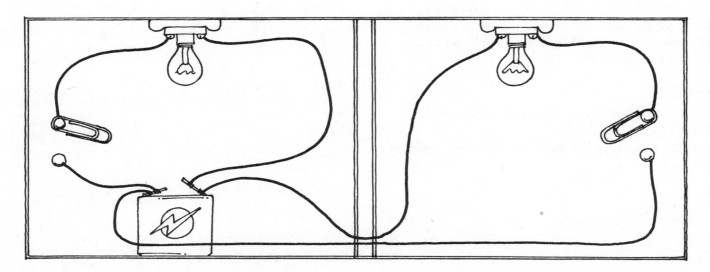

Automatic light

Age range
Seven to eleven.

Group size
Individuals or small groups.

What you need
Completed box house with room divider and lights (see previous activities), adhesive tape, plastic-coated copper wire, drawing pins.

Starting points
- Make sure that the previous tasks are successfully completed.
- Look at various home security systems with automatic lights.
- Talk about street lights which come on when it becomes dark.

Task
Make a door which opens and closes for your house. Next, make a device which will light up your house when the door is opened.

Other information
- The children should use the box house made in the earlier activity.
- This task can be linked to the next through the theme of Home Security.

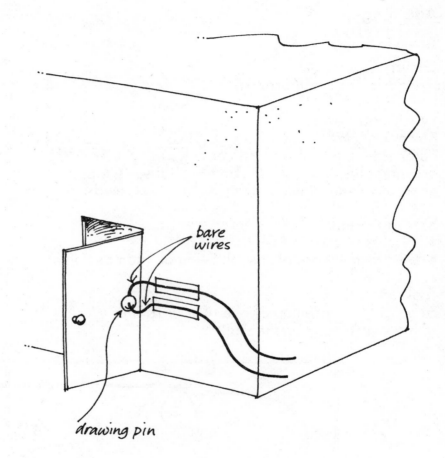

bare wires

drawing pin

Burglar alarm

Age range
Seven to eleven.

Group size
Individuals or small groups.

What you need
Box house from the previous task, plastic-coated copper wire, buzzer or bell, paper clips, adhesive tape, battery.

Starting points
- Talk about a local burglary.
- Discuss neighbourhood watch schemes.
- Collect leaflets from the police station or local library about crime prevention.
- Collect burglar alarm and home security leaflets.
- Read stories: *The Burglar* by David Rees (Arnold Wheaton), *Burglars in the Yard* by Sheila McCullagh (Arnold Wheaton), *Jeffy, the Burglar's Cat* by Ursula Moray Williams (Andersen Press).

Task
A burglar is trying to break into your house. Can you set up an alarm system so that when *either* the door *or* the window is opened the buzzer or the bell sounds?

Other information
- Before beginning the task, the children will have to construct a hinged window in one wall.
- The operation of the alarm when *either* the window *or* the door is opened simulates an electronic circuit known as an OR gate (see the National Curriculum for Science, Attainment Target 12, Level 5, and the associated Programme of Study).

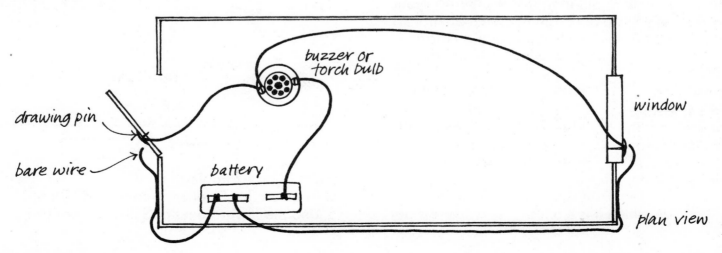

buzzer or torch bulb

drawing pin

bare wire

battery

window

plan view

Stop, thief!

Age range
Seven to eleven.

Group size
Pairs or small groups.

What you need
'Valuable' object eg a heavy vase, 1.5v battery, bulb and bulbholder, buzzer or bell, plastic-coated copper wire, aluminium foil, cardboard, scraps of cloth, foam sponge, pieces of wood, straws, paper clips, paper-fasteners, drawing pins.

Starting points
● Visit a museum or art gallery.
● Have a discussion about antiques.
● Discuss a local burglary and crime prevention.

Task
You have been loaned a valuable vase for a few weeks by a museum. You want to put it on display for everyone in school to see but you do not want it to be stolen. Design and make a device which will sound an alarm if the vase is lifted from the table on which it is standing.

Other information
● The children need to produce a device which is *on* when *not* pressed and *off* when pressed. The easiest solution is to use some kind of springy material which, when compressed, breaks the circuit and when released, completes it.
● The operation of the alarm when the vase is lifted from the base on which it is standing, ie when it is *not*

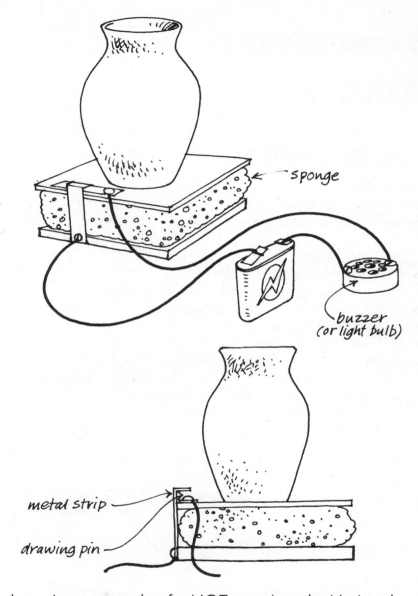

sponge

buzzer (or light bulb)

metal strip

drawing pin

there, is an example of a NOT gate (see the National Curriculum for Science, Attainment Target 12, Level 5, and the Programme of Study for Key Stage 2).

Cover up

Starting points

Topics
- Clothes for different weather conditions eg wet weather, cold weather.
- Clothes for different activities eg climbers, skiers, astronauts.
- Covering up other things eg insulating hot-water tanks.
- Covering up for protection eg from the sun, rain or frost.

Visits
- Market.
- Clothes' store.
- DIY centre.

Stories and rhymes
- *Mrs Mopple's Washing Line* by Anita Hewett (Puffin).
- *The Emperor's New Clothes* (traditional).

Events
- Unusual or extreme weather conditions.

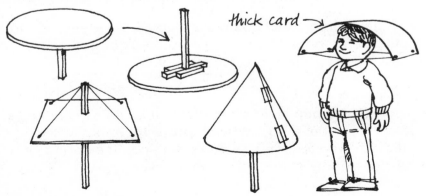

thick card

Rainy days

Age range
Four to seven.

Group size
Individuals or pairs.

What you need
Large sheet of card, large sheet of newspaper, drawing pins, paper fasteners, adhesive tape, garden cane or dowel, string, scissors.

Starting points
- Talk about the weather.
- Discuss the different types of waterproofing.
- Tell the story of Charles Macintosh.
- Read *The Umbrella's Story* by Jez Alborough (Victor Gollancz).

Scenario
Just as you are about to go home from school, it begins to rain *very* heavily. You do not have a hat or coat.

Task
Design and make something to keep your head and shoulders dry while you walk home.

Other information
- Do not use plastic sheets or polythene bags because of the risk of suffocation.
- In the thirteenth century, South American Indians waterproofed their clothing with rubber sap. In 1823, Charles Macintosh invented the macintosh coat, originally made from a layer of rubber between two layers of cloth.

Market stall

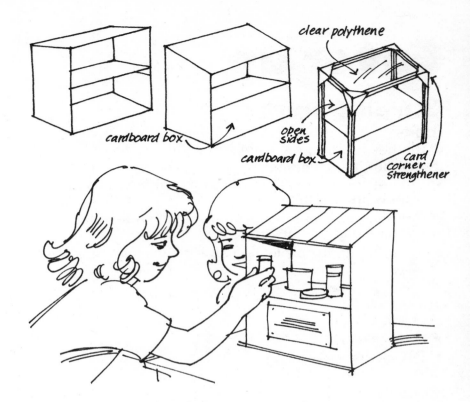

cardboard box

cardboard box

clear polythene

open sides

card corner strengthener

Age range
Four to seven.

Group size
Pairs or small groups.

What you need
Shoe boxes or similar; drawing pins; adhesive and spreaders; stout card from old boxes; materials for canopy, some waterproof, some not; scissors.

Starting points
- Visit a market.
- Discuss pictures of a market.
- Discuss the school fête or summer fair preparations.
- Collect examples of ways to keep sun and rain off things eg umbrella, parasol, pram shade and sun canopies. If the real objects are not available, use a collection of pictures.
- Set up a market corner in the classroom, as an alternative to a shop, with goods for sale.

Scenario
We are going to have a stall at our school fair selling toys, games and books. What will we do to protect our wares from the bright sun or from the rain?

Task
Design and make a stall with a canopy which we can use for the fair.

Other information
- Link this idea to a science topic about water-proofing materials. Through these investigations, the children will be able to choose and use the most appropriate materials from the selection available to them.
- The water-resistance of the stall's canopy can be tested using a watering can or hand spray.
- The shading ability of the canopy can be tested by using a torch if it is not a sunny day.
- The children could complete their stalls by decorating them. The objects for sale could be arranged on a table to represent a small market.

Follow-up
If only one group is doing this task, it could use the large boxes from 'Building a house' (page 18) to make a child-size version. This might be set up in the corner of the classroom as an alternative to a shop.

Eat up

dowel

depth coloured indicator

Starting points

Topics
- Plants.
- Growing things.
- Seeds.
- Farms and farming.
- Food.
- Famine and famine relief.

Visits
- Farm.
- Supermarket.
- Flour mill.
- Garden centre or plant nursery.

Stories and rhymes
- *Jack and the Beanstalk* (Ladybird).
- *The Very Hungry Caterpillar* by Eric Carle (Hamish Hamilton).
- *What-a-Mess* stories by Frank Muir (A & C Black).
- *Growing Vegetable Soup* by L Ehlert (Victor Gollancz).

Events
- Harvest festival.
- Media accounts of famine and third-world needs.
- Food surpluses and the European Community.

Planters

elastic band to indicate depth

Age range
Four to seven.

Group size
Individuals.

What you need
Seed trays, seed compost, various large and small seeds, scraps of wood, including dowel and old pencils.

Starting points
- Discuss where food comes from.
- Discuss time, growth and change.
- Make an autumn seed collection.
- Talk about seeds we eat.
- Collect different grains (wheat, oats, barley), if possible on stalks.
- Talk about harvest time.
- Visit several times a field growing a cereal crop to observe development.

Task
You are going to plant some seeds. You need a planter to make holes the right size to put your seeds in. Design and make a planter.

Other information
- Explain to the children beforehand that seeds must be planted at the right depth.
- Some seeds eg peas and beans, are best pre-soaked to speed up germination.

Garden weeder

Age range
Four to seven.

Group size
Small groups.

What you need
Scraps of wood of varying length and shape, long card tubes, nails, stiff cardboard, florist's wire, string, tools.

Starting points
- Walk around the school garden or visit a local park.
- Collect garden tools.
- Helping the aged by making their lives easier.

Task
Design and make a device which will help to make it easier to weed a garden.

wooden board

Other information
- Set aside a corner of the school garden, or flower beds, a few weeks before the children do this task to allow the weeds to grow.

  Take the children to see it and allow them to pull out the weeds. Point out how tiring this is when you have a large garden or if you are an old person. Use this discussion as the basis for setting the problem.
- You may need to help with the cutting of wood.

Follow-up
Design and make a device to collect the weeds without having to bend over; solutions could include a scoop, a rake or a draw hoe.

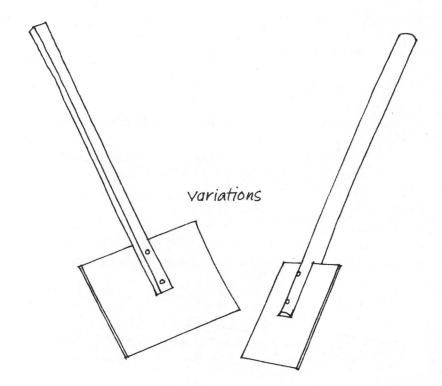

variations

Plant house

Age range
Four to seven.

Group size
Pairs or small groups.

What you need
Plastic lemonade bottles, sheets of clear polythene, cut from old bags, transparent acetate film, assorted sizes of cardboard boxes, containers such as plastic microwave trays to act as seed trays, garden canes, drawing pins, string, tools.

Starting points
- Visit a greenhouse, local garden or garden centre.
- Make a herbarium or bottle garden.
- Grow some plants from seed.

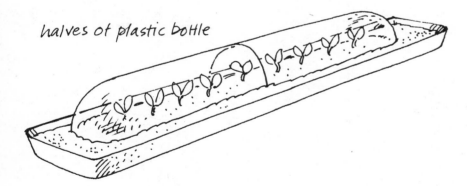

halves of plastic bottle

Other information
- Before the children make a plant house, they need to discuss the conditions needed for plants to grow. This could be linked to a science topic on 'Seeds' or

Task
Design and make a plant house to help the young plants to grow.

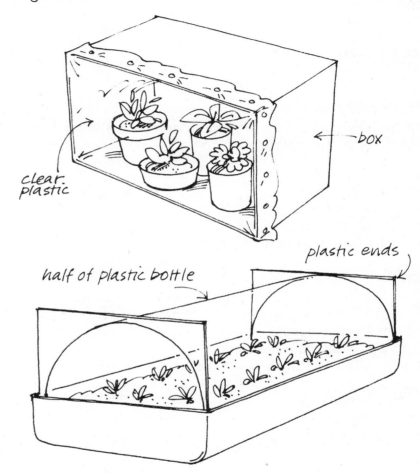

piece of plastic bottle

box

clear plastic

half of plastic bottle

plastic ends

'Growing things'. They should also discuss what is needed to make a successful garden frame or greenhouse.
- Children may need help in cutting the plastic bottles.
- After this task show the children a propagator.

31

Plant waterer

Age range
Six to nine.

Group size
Small groups.

What you need
Assorted plastic containers, plastic tubing, bulldog clips, paper-fasteners, scraps of wood, string, wire, scraps of fabrics, threads and yarns, scissors or snips.

Starting points
- Grow some plants.
- Talk about growing things.
- Talk about caring for living things.

Task
Your seedlings are growing well on the windowsill in the classroom, but your watering can is too big for the job. It gives them too much water at once and might wash them out of the soil. Design and make a plant waterer which will gently water your seeds and young plants.

Other information
Technology is being used here to meet a real need, solving the problem of how to water the plants gently.

margarine tub.

section of bottle, using its handle as a spout

hole in top

section of plastic bottle

plastic tube

plastic bottle

hole in base

Market gardener

Age range
Seven to eleven.

Group size
Whole class.

What you need
Plastic tubs eg from margarine or spread, seed compost, mustard and cress seeds.

Starting points
- Collect packets of seeds.
- Discuss time, growth and change.
- Talk about the harvest festival.
- Talk about the forthcoming autumn fair.
- Take a punnet of mustard and cress with the price still on it and discuss its cost and marketing.

Task
Design and set up a mini-enterprise project – involving the whole class – to produce punnets of mustard and cress for sale at the autumn fair.

Other information
- Collect plastic tubs in large numbers. A wooden or plastic bread tray, lined with aluminium foil, can be used for storage.
- The economic aspects of agricultural technology can be developed through this exercise. The children might consider:
  initial costs of the materials (seeds and compost);
  the time needed for planting to ensure the produce will be ready for the day of the fair;
  how to make a sufficient return on the sale of the punnets of cress to cover costs;
  whether the profit will be used to buy new seeds and compost or given to charity or school funds.

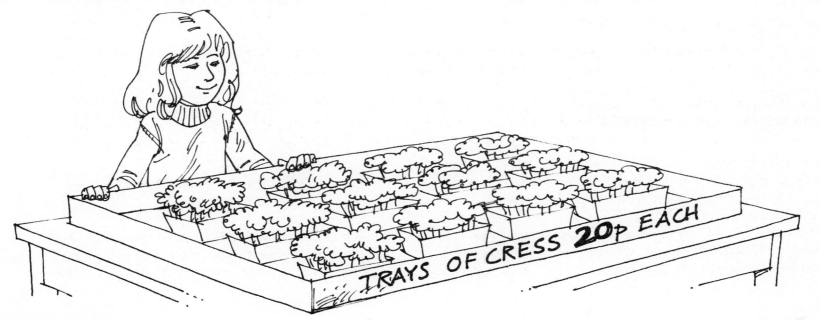

Potato carrier

Age range
Six to nine.

Group size
Pairs or small groups.

What you need
Large, A1 size sheet of newspaper, adhesive tape about 10cm long, two paper clips, 2kg potatoes.

Starting points
- Talk about structures and forces.
- Discuss how to make work easier.
- Tell the story of Margaret Knight.

Scenario
The teacher brings into the classroom about 2kg of potatoes on a tray and tells the class that she has a problem – she does not have a carrier bag in which to carry them home.

Task
Design and make a paper bag to hold the potatoes, from the materials you have been given. The bag should also have a handle for carrying it.

Other information
- Ask the children to make a carrier bag which will carry three or four items from their shop corner.
- Make a collection of bags of different designs and materials. Do this by considering the work of the inventor Margaret Knight, who invented the satchel-bottomed paper bag. See *Footsteps into Science* by

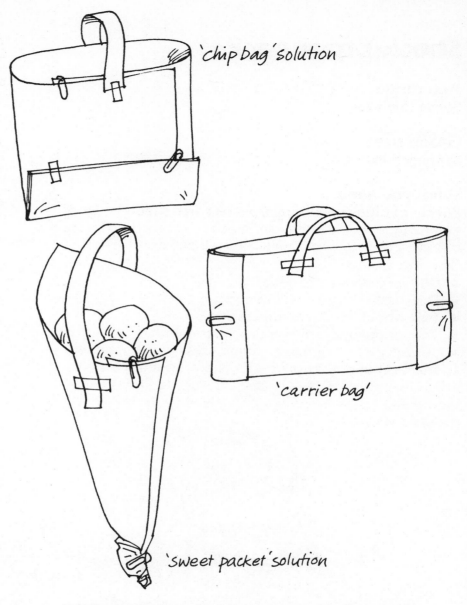

'chip bag' solution

'carrier bag'

'sweet packet' solution

D P and L D Newton, Card 10 (Stanley Thornes).
- The best designs could be mass-produced for use at an autumn fair or other such sale in the school.

Shock-proof packet

Age range
Seven to eleven.

Group size
Small groups.

What you need
Packet of digestive biscuits, two A4 size sheets of card, two A2 size sheets of newspaper, scissors, adhesive tape about 5cm long, two paper clips, elastic band.

Starting points
- Talk about shape and strength.
- Talk about structures and forces.

Scenario
Show the children a packet of biscuits with the biscuits at both ends crushed and broken. Discuss with them the inadequacies of the packaging. Give each child in the group a *whole* biscuit.

Task
Design and make a packet for the biscuits in each group, which will prevent them from breaking if they are dropped from the table to the floor (a height of about one metre).

Other information
- Resources are limited to stimulate imaginative solutions and to encourage their economical use.
- Remind the children that they do not have to use all the materials on offer.
- Similar tasks can be set using other fragile objects such as eggs.
- Alternatively drop an object on it from a height of about one metre. A typical object might be one found in a shopping basket.
- Link this project with science work on strength and shape, and with the structure and function of corrugated materials such as cardboard and metal.

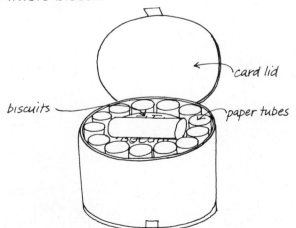

biscuits — card lid — paper tubes

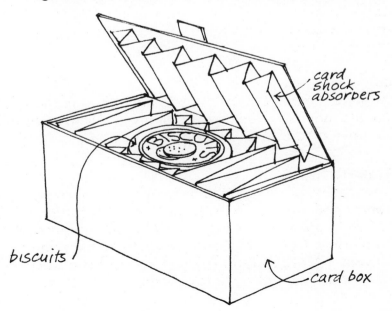

card shock absorbers — biscuits — card box

Egg cup

Age range
Four to eleven.

Group size
Individuals or pairs.

What you need
Straws, pipe-cleaners, wire, cardboard, paper, garden cane, dowel, scraps of wood, 1cm^2 cross-section wood offcuts, egg boxes, small cardboard boxes, scraps of fabrics, yarns and threads, string, scissors, tools, Plasticine.

Starting points
- Talk about food.
- Talk about cookery and egg recipes.
- Talk about Easter eggs.
- Visit a farm that has chickens and ducks.

Task
Design and make a holder for a soft-boiled egg.

Other information
- Give the children access to any other materials that are available.
- Provide some hard-boiled eggs for testing solutions. In the initial stages, you could use modelling-clay eggs or even table-tennis balls.
- The emphasis should be on the quality and appearance of the finished product: it should be functional and attractive.

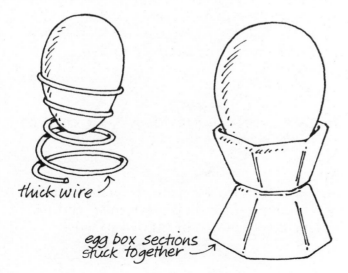

thick wire

egg box sections stuck together

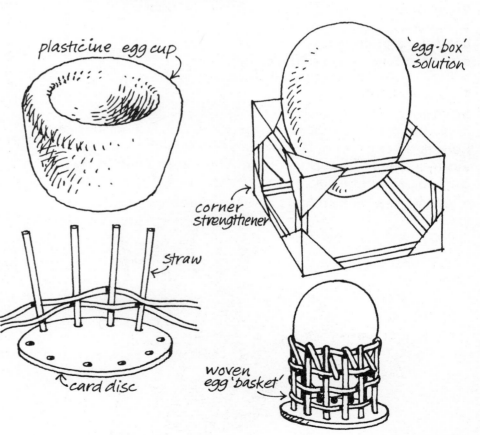

plasticine egg cup

'egg-box' solution

corner strengthener

straw

card disc

woven egg 'basket'

Drink up

Starting points
Topics
- Water.
- The water supply.
- Water pollution.
- Water for life.
- Third World needs: water.

Visits
- Reservoir.
- Water-treatment works.
- Drinks factory.

Stories and rhymes
- *Water* by B Graham and C Humphreys (Blackie).

Events
- Burst water pipe.
- Drought.
- Water-supply problems in other countries.

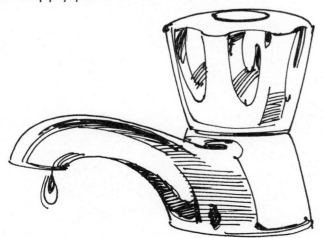

Wishing well

Age range
Six to nine.

Group size
Pairs or small groups.

What you need
Cardboard carpet tube or similar, round plastic tub eg margarine tub, lengths of $1cm^2$ cross-section wood, stout card, florist's wire or similar, thread, adhesive and spreaders, materials for decorating the well, tools.

Starting points
- Visit an old building with a well eg a castle or monastery.
- Talk about water supplies from different sources eg springs, wells, shaduf.
- Read stories and rhymes about wishing wells eg *The Wishing Well Ghost* by Terry-Deary (A & C Black), *The Well Wishers* by Edward Eager (Harcourt Brace Jovanovich), *Jack and Jill* or *Ding Dong Bell* (traditional rhymes).

Task
A photocopiable worksheet is provided for the children on page 111, which takes them through the activity.

Other information
This is a closed problem, designed to show the children a simple way of making a winding mechanism (crank action), with some suggestions for follow-up work.

Rainwater collector

Age range
Four to seven.

Group size
Pairs.

What you need
Polythene sheets cut from bags, plastic bottles, containers of various shapes and sizes, adhesive tape, string, wood offcuts, tools.

Starting points
- Encourage water play.
- Talk about rain.
- Talk about weather recording.
- Discuss the water supply.

Task
Design and make a receptacle to collect as much water as possible during a rain shower.

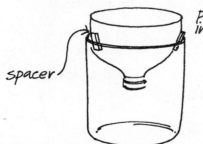

plastic bottle cut into two pieces

spacer

Other information
Encourage the children to recognize the need for a large collecting area and a way of channelling the water into a container.

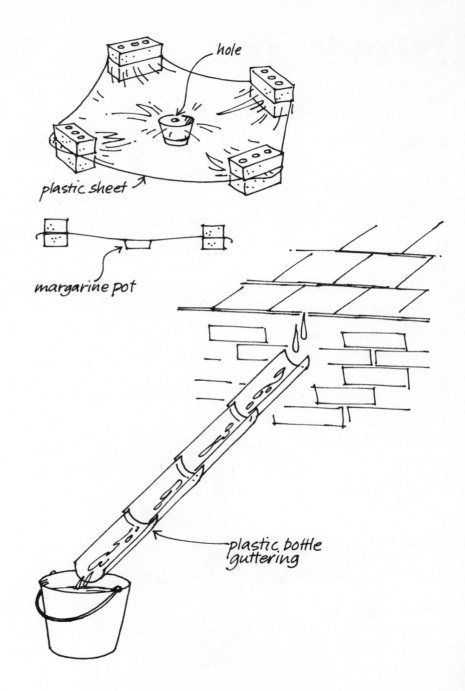

hole

plastic sheet

margarine pot

plastic bottle guttering

Turn on the tap

Age range
Six to nine.

Group size
Small groups.

What you need
Scraps of wood of various shapes and sizes, scraps of metals, scraps of fabrics, nails, elastic bands, drawing pins, wire, tools.

Starting points
- Talk about simple machines that make work easier.
- Discuss social issues, helping and caring eg Help the Aged.

Task
Design and make a device which will help an old person suffering from arthritis to turn on a tap.

Other information
The device is likely to use a simple lever. This activity could follow the activity 'Cocoa time' on page 46.

Follow-up
Introduce spanners and other tools with a similar function. Allow the children to try them.

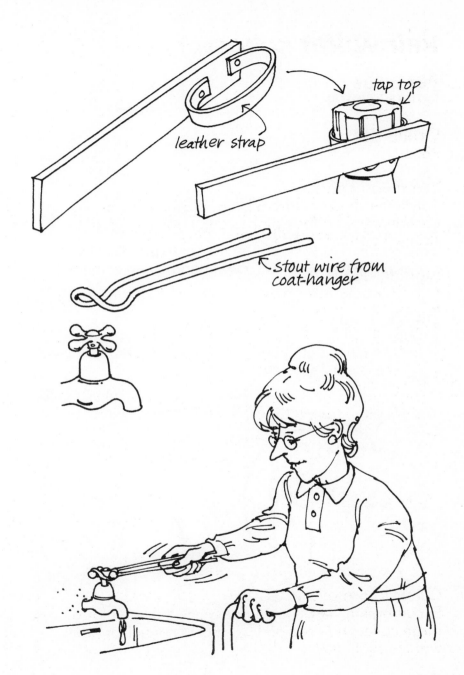

tap top

leather strap

stout wire from coat-hanger

Cup of tea

Age range
Seven to eleven.

Group size
Small groups.

What you need
Pieces of wood, elastic bands, needles, toothpicks, plastic-coated copper wire, crocodile clips, aluminium foil, light bulb and bulbholder, buzzer or bell, 1.5v battery, table tennis balls, pieces of expanded polystyrene foam, straws, cup, teapot filled with *cold* tea.

Starting points
- Talk about the senses.
- Invite visiting speakers from the RNIB, or Guide Dogs for the Blind Association.
- Read stories about the lives of people who were blind eg Helen Keller.
- Introduce Braille.
- Look at warnings in Braille eg on bleach bottles.

Task
Design and make a device which will let blind people know when they have filled the cup with tea.

Other information
- Always use cold liquid to test solutions.
- Useful background work for this topic would be science work on electrical circuits, conductors and insulators, air and water pressure. The children could use their knowledge and understanding in solving the problem.
- Materials should include some unsuitable items such as a light bulb. Children should justify their solutions.

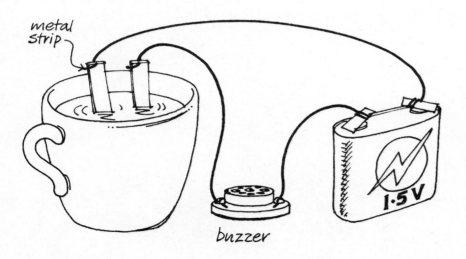

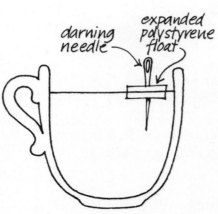

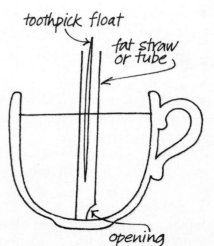

Get up and go

Starting points

Topics
- Ourselves.
- My body.
- Health and hygiene.
- Olympic games.
- Sports and pastimes through the ages.

Visits
- Leisure centre.
- Community health centre.
- Outdoor pursuits centre.

Stories and rhymes
- *Adventure Playground* by Helen Burgess (Hodder and Stoughton).
- *The Pancake Olympics* by Hazel Edwards (Edward Arnold).
- *Bikes in the Air* by Paul Groves and Nigel Grimshaw (Edward Arnold).

Events
- School sports day.
- National or international games.
- Talk by school nurse or health officer.

How hard can you blow?

Age range
Four to eleven.

Group size
Whole class.

What you need
Off-cuts of wood, small balls, selection of paper, card and cardboard, bobbins, nails, dowel or garden cane, plastic containers of different shapes and sizes, plastic tubing, scraps of fabrics, pieces of various metals, wire coat-hangers, wire, scissors or snips, tools.

Starting points
- Let the children make music with wind instruments.
- Talk about windy days: how hard does the wind blow?
- Have a project on 'ourselves' or 'my body'.
- Discuss health education: the anti-smoking campaign.
- Talk about blowing up party balloons.

Task
Design and make a device which will measure how hard you can blow.

Other information
- Use sterilising solution to clean equipment which children put to their lips, as in blowing through a tube.
- If solutions are suggested which involve the child blowing vertically from underneath, they should be modified to prevent her from swallowing anything.

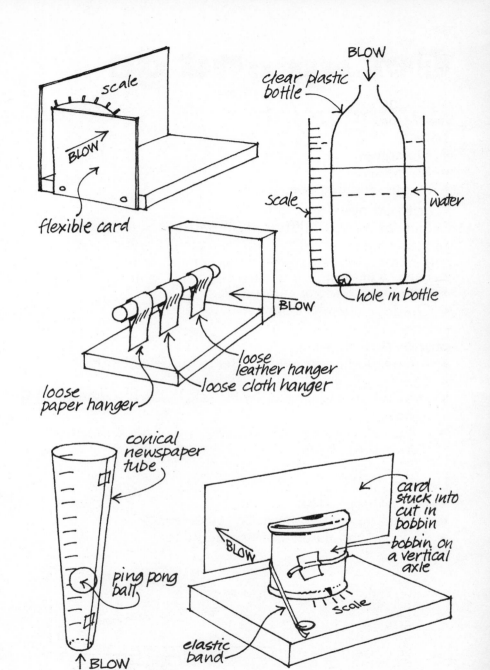

42

Timer

Age range
Six to nine.

Group size
Small groups.

What you need
Offcuts of wood of different shapes and sizes, dowel or garden cane, cardboard, various plastic bottles and containers, adhesive tape, nails, screws, string, thread or yarn, wire, bobbins, bottle tops and jar lids.

Starting points
- Discuss athletics events.
- Talk about skipping as a 'keep fit' exercise.
- Play children's games and recite skipping rhymes.
- Do mathematics work on time.
- Talk about the history of time, clocks and calendars.

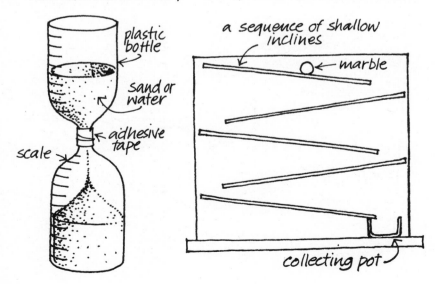

Task
Design and make a device to time your friends. Use it to find out who is the fastest at doing 25 skips.

Other information
Digital watches, which seem so common now, were introduced only in 1971. The use of analogue and digital watches and clocks for timing is required by the National Curriculum for Mathematics, Science, and Design and Technology.

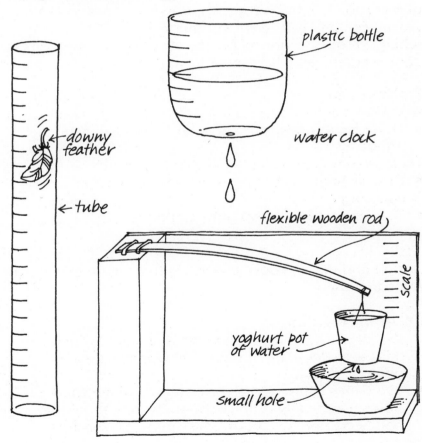

Taking it easy

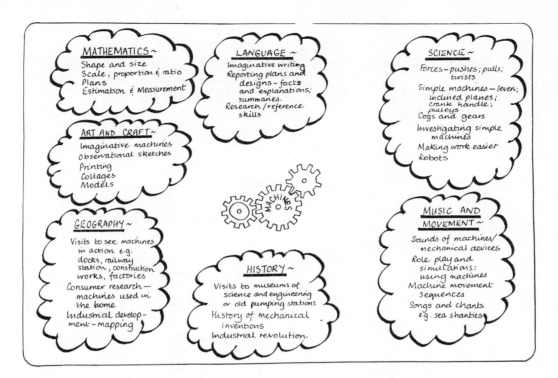

MATHEMATICS ~
Shape and size
Scale, proportion & ratio
Plans
Estimation & Measurement

LANGUAGE ~
Imaginative writing
Reporting plans and
designs - facts
and explanations;
summaries.
Research/reference
skills

SCIENCE ~
Forces - pushes; pulls;
twists
Simple machines - levers;
inclined planes;
crank handle;
pulleys
Cogs and gears
Investigating simple
machines
Making work easier
Robots

ART AND CRAFT ~
Imaginative machines
Observational sketches
Printing
Collages
Models

MACHINES

GEOGRAPHY ~
Visits to see machines
in action e.g.
docks, railway
station, construction
works, factories
Consumer research —
machines used in
the home
Industrial develop-
ment - mapping

HISTORY ~
Visits to museums of
science and engineering
or old pumping stations
History of mechanical
inventions
Industrial revolution

MUSIC AND MOVEMENT ~
Sounds of machines/
mechanical devices
Role play and
simulations:
using machines
Machine movement
sequences
Songs and chants
e.g. sea shanties

Power to your elbow

Starting points

Topics
- Moving around.
- On the move.
- Making work easier.
- Machines.

Visits
- School kitchen.
- Farm.
- Building site.
- Factory.
- Fairground.

Stories and rhymes
- *Professor Branestawm* stories by Norman Hunter (Puffin).
- *The Municipal Inventor of Barbaria* by John Broughton (Arnold Wheaton).
- *Complete Adventures of Charlie and Mr Willie Wonka* by Roald Dahl (Unwin Hyman).
- *Stone Age Magic* by Brian Ball (Hamish Hamilton).

Events
- Roadworks.
- Building work near the school.
- Caretaker doing repairs with his toolkit.

Cocoa time

Age range
Four to seven.

Group size
Pairs or small groups.

What you need
Cocoa tin with lid which levers off, collection of appropriate and inappropriate solutions, for example, spoon, screwdriver, wooden spoon, knitting needle.

Starting points
- Discuss how to make jobs easier.
- Make a collection of kitchen tools.

Scenario and task
Today at playtime, we are going to have a hot chocolate drink but I cannot get the lid off the tin. Can you find a way to do this for me?

Other information
- The aim of this simple task is to introduce the lever as a basic machine which makes work easier.
- Having solved the problem, ask the children to look for other places in and around the classroom where levers are used eg in levers to stop/start toys, bucket or beam balances, spades in the sand pit and door handles.

spoon as lever

INKING
COLATE

Chopsticks

Age range
Six to nine.

Group size
Individuals or pairs.

What you need
Long, thin pieces of wood, or jelutong, about 20 cm long, garden cane, art straws, nails, elastic bands, paper-fasteners.

Starting points
- Discuss objects that make work easier.
- Talk about food.
- Collect a set of chopsticks.

Scenario
You are having a Chinese meal and are given two chopsticks to eat with. You cannot use them.

Task
Invent a way of improving the chopsticks so that you can use them with one hand to pick up something very small, like a grain of rice.

Other information
- The task develops the children's understanding of levers as machines.
- Each child will need a pair of sticks to begin the task.
- Show the children a collection of implements with pivots, either when they have finished the task or earlier if you feel they need help with the solution. The collection could include scissors, pliers, pincers, nut-crackers and eyelash curlers.

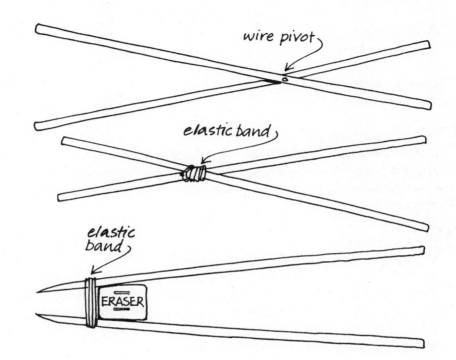

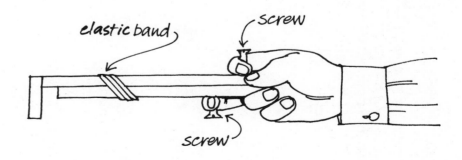

Lift up

Age range
Seven to eleven.

Group size
Small groups.

What you need
Pieces of wood of different shapes and sizes, assorted cardboard boxes, bobbins, string, thread or yarn, lids, wire, corrugated cardboard from large boxes, adhesive and spreaders, adhesive tape, tools.

Starting points
- Discuss how to make work easier.
- Talk about machines and construction works.
- Observe machines for lifting, pulling and winding, like cranes or car-recovery vehicles with winches or well mechanisms.
- Collect pictures of machines winding, lifting etc.

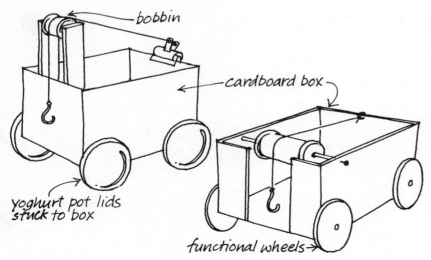

bobbin

cardboard box

yoghurt pot lids stuck to box

functional wheels →

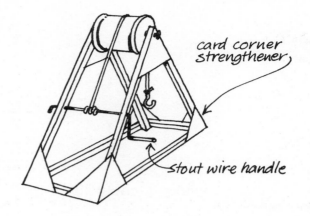

card corner strengthener

stout wire handle

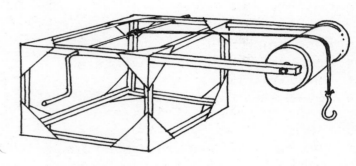

Task
Design and make a crane which will lift a weight of 100g, one metre from the floor.

Other information
- The task introduces the idea of the pulley. With older or more able children, this can be developed into the winding mechanism of the crank.
- Most children will come up with a hand-operated mechanical solution, but older ones might consider an electrical solution, using a battery-operated motor.
- Cranes date from the Ancient World and were used in Roman times. The derrick crane, with a slanting arm, was invented in the fifteenth century.

Grain mover

Age range
Seven to eleven.

Group size
Small groups.

What you need
Plastic bottles and containers of various shapes and sizes, various-sized cardboard boxes, sheets of plastic, fabric, card and paper, string, adhesive and spreaders, adhesive tape, string or yarn, tin cans, bobbins, dowel or garden cane, straws, old pencils or crayons, sand or rice, tools.

Starting points
- Discuss how the work can be made easier.
- Talk about machines.
- Talk about transport.
- Discuss food and farming.

Task
The problem is provided as a photocopiable worksheet (page 112).

Other information
- The task is intended to build up expertise in designing and making simple moving machines. The children will need to draw on their previous experiences of making work easier.
- The problem could be linked to topic work on mining or quarrying.

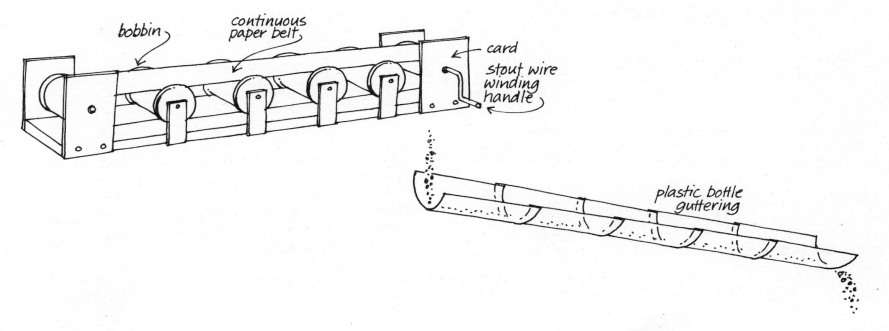

Helping hand

Age range
Seven to eleven.

Group size
Individuals or pairs.

What you need
Lengths of wood, dowel or cane, pieces of plastic or
rubber tubing, lengths of craft or florist's wire,
cardboard tubes such as from rolls of cooking foil,
sheets of cardboard cut from boxes, nails or screws,
adhesive and spreaders, adhesive tape, Blu-tak, scissors
or snips, tools.

Starting points
- Introduce religious and moral education: for
  example caring; Help the Aged.
- Take the opportunity which arises from a child
  breaking a leg. Point out how difficult it is for her to
  bend down.

Task
Design and make a device which will help someone in a
wheelchair – or who cannot bend – to pick up an object
he has dropped on the floor.

Other information
Test the device with a collection of objects of various
shapes and sizes that need to be picked up from the
floor, for example a handkerchief, a letter, a knitting
needle or a sweet.

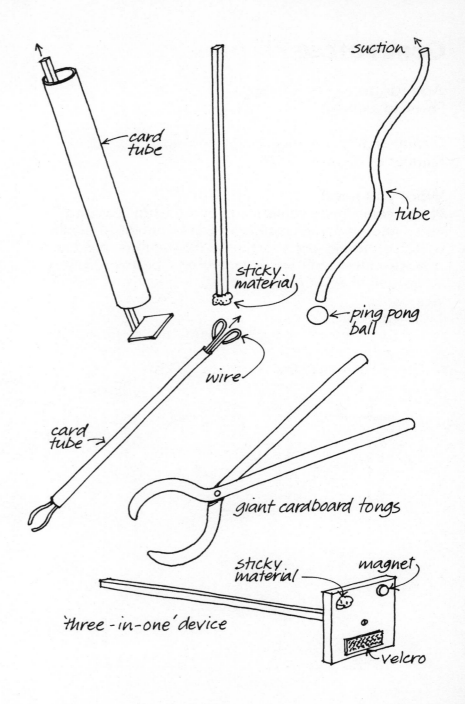

card tube

suction

sticky material

tube

ping pong ball

wire

card tube

giant cardboard tongs

sticky material

magnet

'three-in-one' device

velcro

Coin sorter

Age range
Seven to eleven.

Group size
Pairs or small groups.

What you need
Plastic coins to the value of 1p, 5p and 10p, scraps of wood, pieces of thick cardboard cut from large boxes, assorted plastic containers, cardboard tubes, adhesive and spreaders, adhesive tape, string or yarn, nails or screws, stout scissors or snips, tools.

Starting points
- Set up a shop or post office in the classroom and let the children relate their shopping experiences.
- Carry out maths work on money.
- Discuss what you need for a fairground (pages 96, 97).

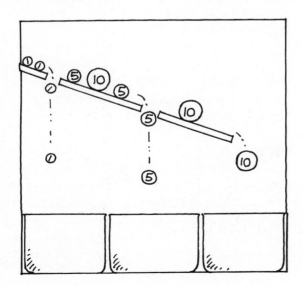

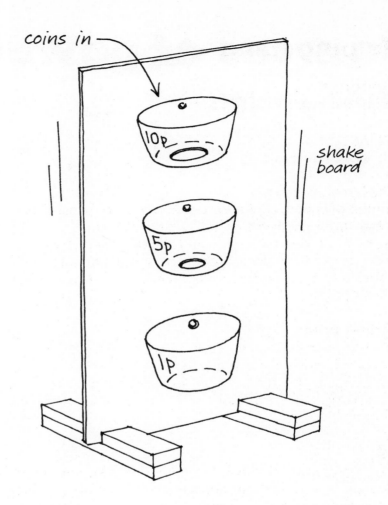

Task
Design and make a device which will sort a mixed bag of coins into lots of 1p, 5p and 10p.

Other information
- The device should be one that makes work easier.
- The task could also be done in connection with the work on the fairground (see pages 96 and 97).

51

Sources of power

Starting points

Topics
- Wind.
- Water.
- Energy.
- Alternative energy.
- The North Sea.
- Moving through air.

Visits
- Windmill.
- Watermill.
- Steam railway.
- Traction engine rally.
- Power station.

Stories and rhymes
- *Elidor* by Alan Garner (Armada).

Events
- Very windy days.
- Kites.
- Air-sea rescue.

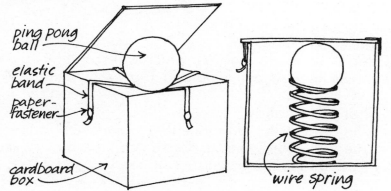

ping pong ball

elastic band

paper-fastener

cardboard box

wire spring

Jumping frogs

Age range
Four to seven.

Group size
Individuals.

What you need
Sheets of plain card cut from empty cereal boxes, small cardboard boxes eg tea-bag boxes, scissors, elastic bands, springs, scraps of sponge, table-tennis or polystyrene ball, adhesive and spreaders, coloured crayons or pens.

Starting points
- Look at a toy Jack-in-the-box.
- Look at toys which store energy, for example animals which bounce on a spring, birds and aeroplanes which have an elastic band to make them fly, pogo sticks, space hoppers.
- Talk about children's toys through the ages.
- Visit a toy museum.

Task
Ask the children to follow the photocopiable worksheet on page 113. Then ask them to design and make an animal which jumps out of a box.

Other information
- The first part of the task is for the children to understand how energy is stored in an elastic band.
- Other means of propulsion for the animal-in-the-box include springs, thick rubber, compressible sponge and folded stout card. The children could make the animal from a polystyrene or table-tennis ball.

People power

Age range
Four to seven.

Group size
Pairs.

What you need
For a child-sized trial: large cardboard box, three broom handles (each cut in half to make six rollers), length of rope. For the children's task: small pieces of wood, dowel or garden cane, cross-section wood about 1cm^2, straws, small cardboard boxes, corrugated cardboard from boxes, string, bobbins, card or wood wheels, wire, plastic bottles, polystyrene or soft balls.

Starting points
- Talk about how the Ancient Egyptians used rollers to move heavy loads. Use a model to demonstrate the technique before allowing the children to begin their task.
- Talk about the history of the motor car.
- Collect pictures and/or objects which we push or pull.

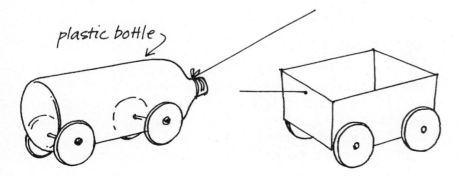

plastic bottle

Task
Design and make a buggy with wheels which moves freely when it is pushed or pulled.

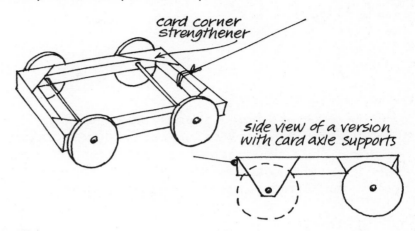

card corner strengthener

side view of a version with card axle supports

Follow-up
Older or more able children might like to think about fitting some sort of suspension system to the buggy so that it will ride smoothly on bumpy roads.

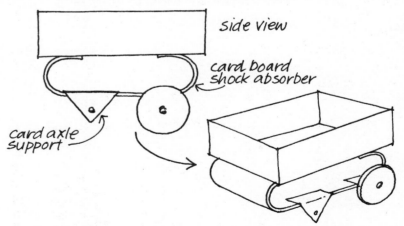

side view

card board shock absorber

card axle support

The task leads naturally into looking for alternative ways to power the buggy.

The pull of gravity

Age range
Seven to eleven.

Group size
Pairs or small groups.

What you need
Offcuts of wood of different shapes and sizes, large cardboard box, string or yarn, matchbox, dowel, garden cane or pencil, bobbin, yoghurt pot, sand or marbles as weight, long card tube, stout corrugated cardboard, paper-fasteners, adhesive tape, scissors or snips.

Starting points
- Carry out science-based work on forces and gravity.
- Arrange to use a lift.
- Discuss the problems of multi-storey buildings for people in wheelchairs.

Task
The task is provided in the photocopiable worksheet on page 114. The first part of the sheet sets the scene and gives the children the background information they need. Then the problem is presented: to design and make a model lift.

Other information
- The children need to know a little about gravity. The initial activity provides the background and is followed by the technological problem.
- The children are introduced to the conversion of stored energy as an object falls.
- Lifts have been used in mines since ancient times, but these were dangerous. Safe passenger lifts came into use in a New York shop in 1857.

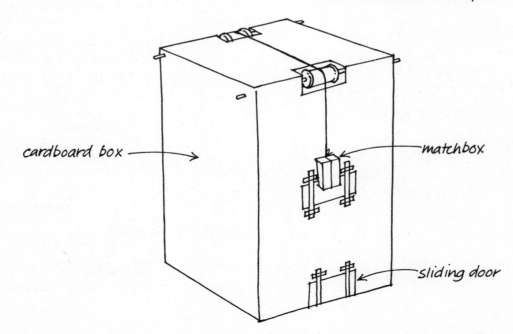

cardboard box

matchbox

sliding door

Energy from falling water

Age range
Seven to eleven.

Group size
Pairs or small groups.

What you need
Scraps of wood, dowel or garden cane, plastic bottles and containers, stout cardboard, corrugated plastic, string or yarn, bobbins, assorted tubs and lids, adhesive and spreaders, adhesive tape, tools.

Starting points
- Discuss the topic of energy.
- Discuss alternative energy sources.
- Talk about water.
- Talk about hydro-electricity.
- Visit a watermill.

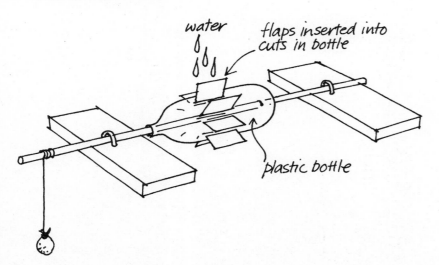

water

flaps inserted into cuts in bottle

plastic bottle

Task
Design and make a waterwheel, or water turbine, which will make a rod spin. What can it be used for? Have your waterwheel do useful work.

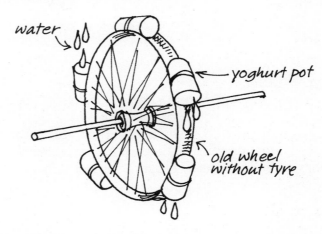

water

yoghurt pot

old wheel without tyre

Other information
- The solutions show overshot wheels, which can be operated using water from a tap or hosepipe.
- The energy is produced from gravity, the water falling in response to the pull of gravity.
- The first, or 'Norse', mill had a vertical axle, and the wheel lay flat on the river bed, turning horizontally.

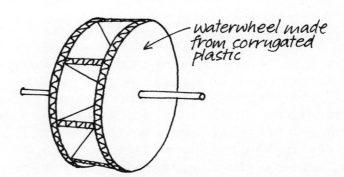

waterwheel made from corrugated plastic

Tower crane

Age range
Seven to eleven.

Group size
Small groups.

What you need
Offcuts of wood of different shapes and sizes, lengths of jelutong or cross-section wood about $1cm^2$, dowel or garden cane, nails and screws, string or yarn, eye screws, bobbins, cardboard, card, adhesive and spreaders, adhesive tape, plastic-coated copper wire, battery, small electric motor.

Starting points
- Look at and discuss construction work, for example a new road, a bridge, a building or an office block.
- Talk about structures and forces.
- Collect pictures of cranes and other large machines at work on a building site.

Other information
- Show the children what a tower crane looks like before starting on the task.
- When the crane picks up the load (a weight of about half a kilo) it may tilt, so the children will need to remedy this instability. In practice, a tower crane has a counterbalance on the arm opposite the load.
- The children should compare the cranes they make with real ones. In particular, they should notice the triangular lattice structures used for strength. This activity can lead to science-based work which involves testing the strength of different shapes.

Task
Design and make a tower crane to span the gap between two desks. It should lift and carry a load from one desk to the other.

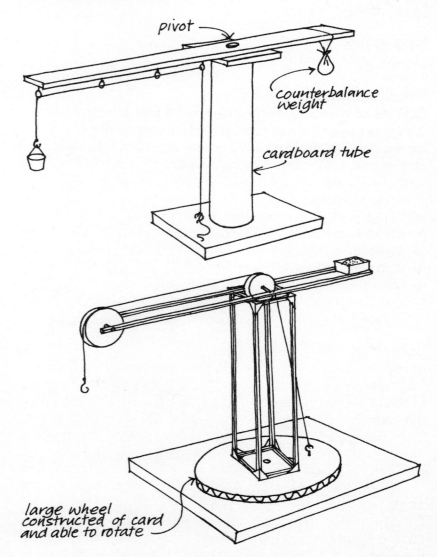

Maroon

Age range
Seven to eleven.

Group size
Individuals or pairs.

What you need
Offcuts of wood of different shapes and sizes, elastic band, strips of wire, strips of stiff plastic, cardboard tubes, card, adhesive and spreaders, nails and screws, paper clips, paper-fasteners, drawing pins, tools, small polystyrene balls for testing.

Starting points
- Introduce a history project, for example, the Romans, in which weapons and battles are important.
- Talk about ballistae and projectiles.
- Talk about shipwrecks and the use of flares.
- Discuss the various rescue groups, for example RNLI (Royal National Lifeboat Institution).

Scenario
Imagine that there has been a storm at sea and a ship has been wrecked on the rocks. You are members of a lifeboat rescue team. You must set up a device to rescue the people from the ship. Do this by firing a strong rope from the lifeboat to the ship, where it can be fastened. The people can then escape using the rope. Such a device is called a maroon.

Task
Design and make a device which will fire a rope, in this case a length of string, from the lifeboat – your desk – to the ship – your neighbour's desk – two metres away.

Remember, if the rope *does not* land on the ship, you must fire again. Time is important, since people's lives are in danger! You must make sure your device fires as accurately as possible.

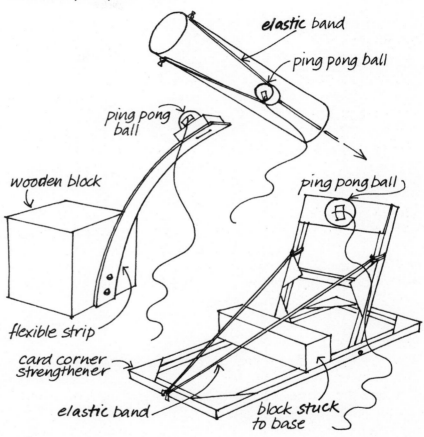

elastic band
ping pong ball
ping pong ball
wooden block
ping pong ball
flexible strip
card corner strengthener
elastic band
block stuck to base

Other information
- The accuracy of the device in firing and reaching its target should be considered.
- This task requires both the use and control of an energy source.
- The children should wear safety spectacles.

Out and about

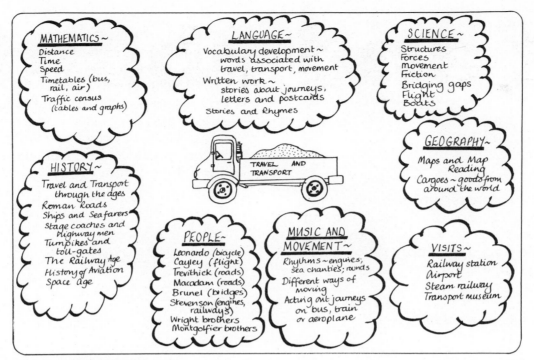

MATHEMATICS~
Distance
Time
Speed
Timetables (bus, rail, air)
Traffic census (tables and graphs)

LANGUAGE~
Vocabulary development~ words associated with travel, transport, movement
Written work ~ stories about journeys, letters and postcards
Stories and Rhymes

SCIENCE~
Structures
Forces
Movement
Friction
Bridging gaps
Flight
Boats

HISTORY~
Travel and Transport through the ages
Roman Roads
Ships and Seafarers
Stage coaches and Highwaymen
Turnpikes and toll-gates
The Railway Age
History of Aviation
Space Age

GEOGRAPHY~
Maps and Map Reading
Cargoes ~ goods from around the world

PEOPLE~
Leonardo (bicycle)
Cayley (flight)
Trevithick (roads)
Macadam (roads)
Brunel (bridges)
Stevenson (engines, railways)
Wright brothers
Montgolfier brothers

MUSIC AND MOVEMENT~
Rhythms ~ engines; sea chanties; rounds
Different ways of moving
Acting out journeys on bus, train or aeroplane

VISITS~
Railway station
Airport
Steam railway
Transport museum

People carriers

Starting points

Topics
- Water.
- Floating and sinking.
- Roads.
- Railways.
- Transport through the ages.
- Voyages of exploration, for example, Christopher Columbus.

Visits
- Seaside.
- Harbour.
- Railway station.
- Airport.

Stories and rhymes
- *Who Sank the Boat?* by P Allen (Hamish Hamilton).
- *Mr Gumpy's Outing* by John Burningham (Puffin).
- *Chitty Chitty Bang Bang* by Ian Fleming (Collins).

Events
- Steam and traction engine rallies.
- Sailing events, for example round-the-world yacht race; tall ships' race.
- Air shows.
- Hot-air balloon or airship.

Boats

Age range
Four to seven.

Group size
Individuals or pairs.

What you need
Assorted plastic cartons and trays, plastic bottles, metal trays, assorted lids, straws, scraps of wood of different shapes and sizes, pieces of card, modelling clay, pieces of expanded polystyrene packaging, paper, dowel or garden cane, string or yarn, tools, water trough.

Starting points
- Talk about water and its properties.
- Talk about floating and sinking.
- Let the children recount a visit to the seaside.
- Visit a harbour, or talk about a visit to a harbour.
- Read stories, for example *Humphrey's Bear* by Jan Wahl (Victor Gollancz).
- Recite rhymes eg *The Owl and the Pussycat*.

Task
Design and make a boat to cross a water trough.

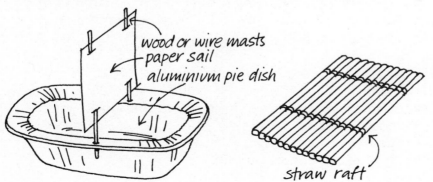

wood or wire masts
paper sail
aluminium pie dish

straw raft

Other information
- The task is simple and allows the children free imagination in their solutions. It gives an opportunity to discuss why things float, the consequences of overloading a boat, what gives a boat the power to move and the best shape for efficient movement.
- The earliest evidence of water transport is a paddle, probably from a dug-out canoe, found in Yorkshire and dating from about 7,500 BC.

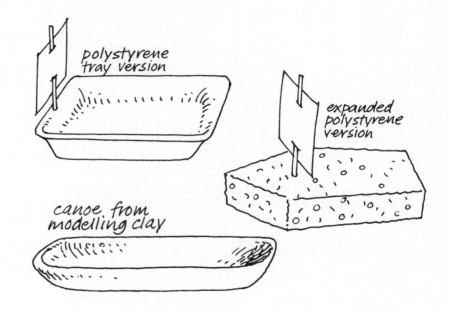

polystyrene tray version

expanded polystyrene version

canoe from modelling clay

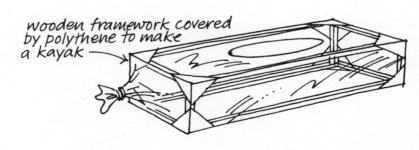

wooden framework covered by polythene to make a kayak

Powered boats

Age range
Seven to eleven.

Group size
Small groups.

What you need
Scraps of wood of different shapes and sizes, dowel or garden cane, nails and screws, elastic bands, plastic propellers, plastic-coated copper wire, small electric motor, battery, card, string or thread, balloons, assorted plastic bottles and containers, straws, paper clips, paper fasteners, adhesive and spreaders, adhesive tape, tools.

Starting points
- Talk about water.
- Talk about energy and power.
- Talk about sea voyages.
- Explain navigation.
- Discuss sailing races eg the Americas Cup, Cowes week.
- Read *Sir Francis Drake – His Daring Deeds* by Roy Gerard (Victor Gollancz).

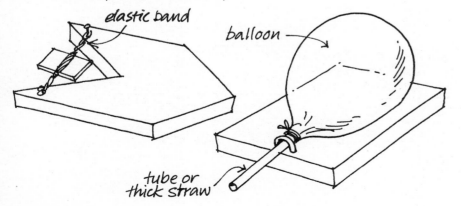

Task
You are going to enter a race. Design and make a small, powered boat which will go the furthest distance as quickly as possible under its own power.

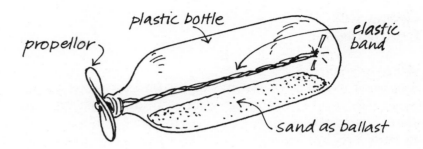

Other information
- When the children have finished their designs, let them hold a competition to test them.
- If possible, have a long piece of guttering, about 3m long, and sealed at both ends, to act as the test trough. If this is not available, then a water trough, or long lightweight polystyrene garden trough, available from garden centres, is useful.
- You may need to limit the overall dimensions of the boat, depending upon the test trough.

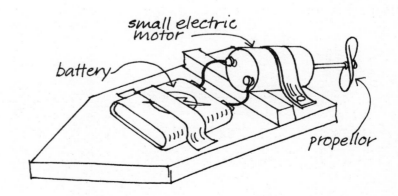

Self-righting boats

Age range
Seven to eleven.

Group size
Small groups.

What you need
Scraps of wood of different shapes and sizes, assorted plastic trays and containers, pieces of dowel or garden cane, card, screws or nails, wire, modelling clay, marbles, various weights, adhesive and spreaders, scraps of fabric, including net, tools.

Starting points
- Look at ships and navigation.
- Explain floating and sinking.
- Talk about balance and the centre of gravity.
- Discuss voyages of exploration.
- Look at leisure and water sports.
- Explain the work of the RNLI.
- Discuss modern lifeboats, which are self-righting.
- Read stories of sea disasters, for example the Grace Darling story, the *Titanic*, the *Marie Celeste*.

Task
Design and make a model boat which will right itself if it capsizes.

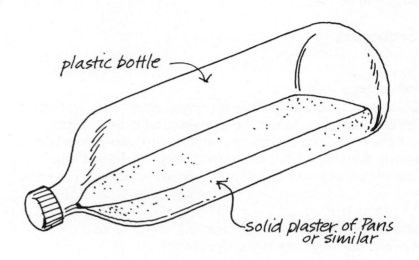

plastic bottle

solid plaster of Paris or similar

Other information
- The activity will lead the children towards understanding the purpose of the keel on a boat.
- The first self-righting lifeboat was built in the mid-nineteenth century.

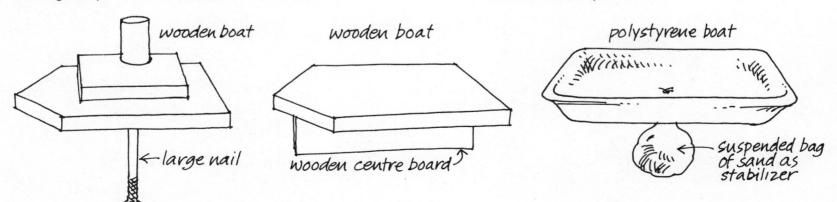

wooden boat — ←large nail

wooden boat — wooden centre board

polystyrene boat — suspended bag of sand as stabilizer

Land yacht

Age range
Seven to eleven.

Group size
Pairs or small groups.

What you need
Scraps of wood of different shapes and sizes, assorted plastic trays and containers, pieces of cross-section wood about 1cm^2, card, adhesive and spreaders, dowel or garden cane, wheels or materials to make them, thread or string, small cardboard boxes, straws, tools.

Starting points
- Look at how energy is created from the wind.
- Talk about movement and forces.
- Ask the children about their hobbies.
- Discuss the theme of transport on land through the ages.

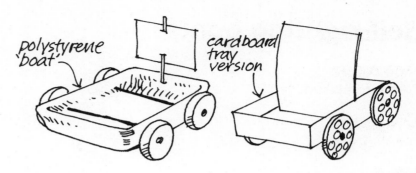

polystyrene 'boat'

cardboard tray version

Task
Design and make a fast land yacht.

Other information
- Wind can be simulated by using a small battery-operated, hand-held fan.
- The children should be allowed to test their designs in an open area, like the school hall.

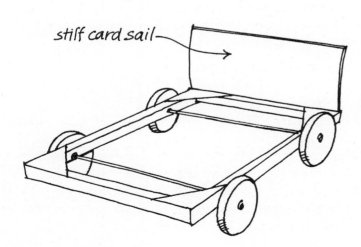

stiff card sail

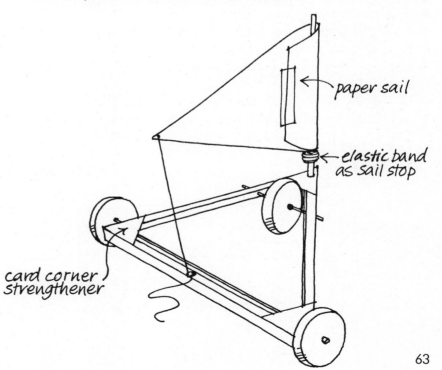

paper sail

elastic band as sail stop

card corner strengthener

Scooter

Age range
Seven to eleven.

Group size
Small groups.

What you need
Scraps of wood of different shapes and sizes, dowel or garden cane, straws, pieces of cross-section wood about 1cm^2, wheels or materials to make them, screws and nails, adhesive and spreaders, wire, tools.

Starting points
- Look at a child's scooter.
- Visit a retail toy centre.

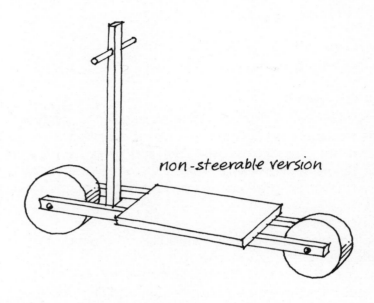

non-steerable version

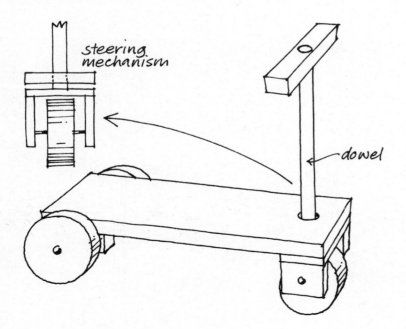

steering mechanism

dowel

Task
Design and make a scooter.

Other information
- Let the children choose whether the scooter will have two or three wheels.
- With older children, make the problem more difficult by asking them to make the scooter steerable.
- The motorized scooter became popular in the 1950s and 1960s. Use this information in a history topic on 'how we used to live'.

Ferry

Age range
Six to nine.

Group size
Pairs or small groups.

What you need
Assorted plastic cartons and trays, straws, scraps of wood, bobbins, pieces of expanded polystyrene packaging, dowel or garden cane, string or yarn, nails, tools.

Starting points
- Do work on travel and transport.
- Talk about bridges.
- Tell the children myths and legends concerning ferries eg Charon, the ferryman of the River Styx.

Scenario
The bridge connecting Bird Island to the mainland has been washed away during the winter storms. The river level is rising, and the island will soon be totally under water. The people of the island are in great danger and must be rescued, but there are no boats or helicopters available. It is up to you and your team to rescue them.

Task
Design and make a two-way, rope-operated ferry which can be used to rescue the island inhabitants.

Other information
- Work on and push and pull forces is a useful starting point.
- Some computer programs simulate this task, usually in the context of crossing a river.

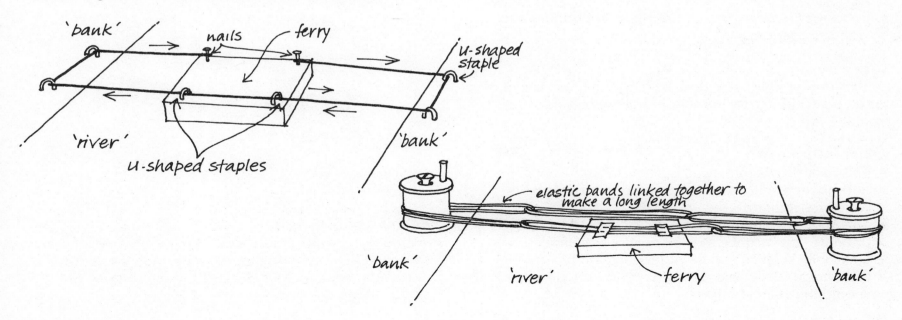

65

Wheeled vehicle

Age range
Six to nine.

Group size
Individuals or pairs.

What you need
Scraps of wood of different shapes and sizes, assorted plastic trays and containers, pieces of cross-section wood about $1cm^2$, card, adhesive and spreaders, dowel or garden cane, wheels or materials to make them, thread or string, small cardboard boxes, tools.

Starting points
- Have a topic about the history of travel on land.
- Talk about moving around.
- Discuss the topic of energy.
- Read *Mr Gumpy's Motor Car* by John Burningham (Jonathan Cape).

Task
Design and make a wheeled vehicle which will travel as far as possible across the school hall when released from the top of a slope.

Other information
- This task draws upon and consolidates the children's earlier experiences of designing and making objects which move in different ways.
- The quality of the finished product should be based upon its appearance as well as its performance.
- Links with science can be made through fair testing the vehicles. Why use a ramp? Where on the slope should the vehicles start?

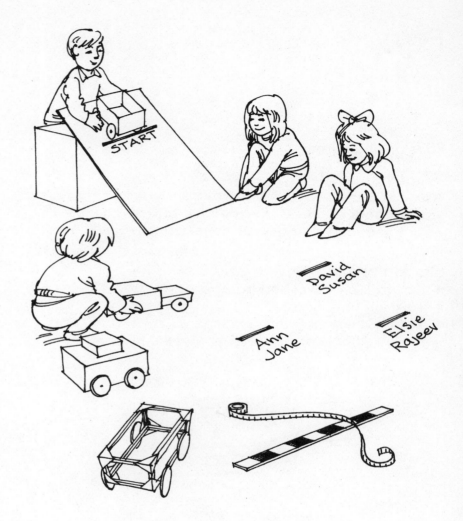

Follow-up
With older, or more able, children introduce economics by giving them a budget and charging them for the materials they use. This stresses the importance of the design stage.

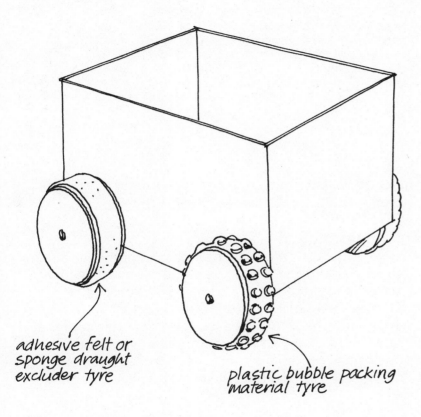

adhesive felt or sponge draught excluder tyre

plastic bubble packing material tyre

Roughrider

Age range
Six to nine.

Group size
Pairs or small groups.

What you need
Small cardboard box, cane or rods to act as axles, material to make wheels, such as bubble plastic, elastic bands, sponge balls, draught excluder.

Starting points
- Talk about travel and transport.
- Look at the history of roads through the ages.
- Discuss the topic of forces.
- Talk about stretching and elasticity.

Task
Design and make a vehicle with wheels which will absorb shocks encountered when travelling across bumpy ground.

Other information
- There are often several solutions to a problem. One is to smooth the road. In this task, an alternative – smoothing the vehicle – is presented. Let the children make wheels and then modify them so that they are suitable for rough roads.
- The task is suitable for children who have already made a wheeled vehicle.
- Leather tyres were used on Ancient Egyptian chariots more than 3,000 years ago. Solid rubber and pneumatic tyres were invented during the middle of the nineteenth century.

Self-propelled vehicle

Age range
Seven to eleven.

Group size
Small groups.

What you need
Scraps of wood, assorted plastic trays and containers, pieces of cross-section wood about 1cm², card, adhesive and spreaders, dowel or garden cane, wheels or materials to make them, thread or string, small cardboard boxes, small electric motor, plastic-coated copper wires, battery, elastic bands, modelling clay, assorted weights, plastic propeller, balloons, bobbins, tools.

Starting points
- Talk about travel on land.
- Look at the history of transport through the ages.
- Look at the history of the motorcar.
- Carry out work on energy.
- Discuss vintage car rallies, for example the London to Brighton rally.

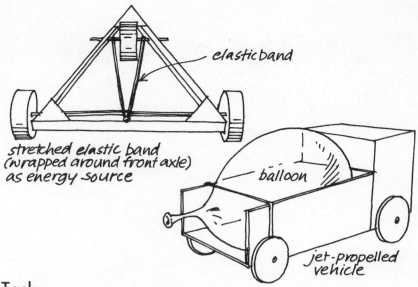

stretched elastic band
(wrapped around front axle)
as energy source

elastic band

balloon

jet-propelled vehicle

Task
The challenge is set for the children on the photocopiable worksheet on page 115.

Other information
- Give the children plastic money and put someone in charge of the DIY shop to sell the materials which have been priced.
- To assess the task, you should consider: the economics (mathematics work on cost per centimetre of wood etc); the appearance of the vehicle; and its performance (the time it takes to travel a fixed distance or the distance it can travel in a fixed time).

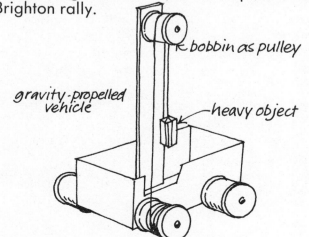

bobbin as pulley

gravity-propelled vehicle

heavy object

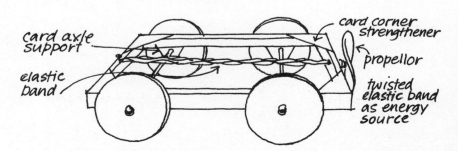

card axle support

card corner strengthener

propellor

elastic band

twisted elastic band as energy source

Moving materials

Starting points

Topics
- Transport through the ages.
- Moving around.
- Making work easier.
- Machines.
- Building site.

Visits
- Factory.
- Building or construction site.
- Transport or railway museum.

Stories and rhymes
- *Billy the Bulldozer* by Boswell Taylor (Hodder and Stoughton).
- *The Princess and the Steamroller* by Boswell Taylor (Hodder and Stoughton).

Events
- Harvest time.
- Deliveries of goods to school.

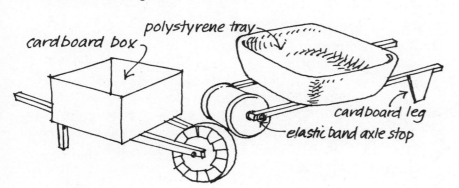

cardboard box

polystyrene tray

cardboard leg

elastic band axle stop

Wheelbarrow

Age range
Four to seven.

Group size
Pairs.

What you need
Scraps of wood of different shapes and sizes, pieces of card and cardboard, bobbins, screws and nails, small cardboard boxes, assorted plastic trays and containers, wheels or materials to make them, pieces of plastic tubing, craft or florist's wire, string or yarn, adhesive tape, tools.

Starting points
- Talk about how to make work easier.
- List objects that move around.
- Carry out work in the school garden.
- Talk about Harvest festival.
- Visit garden festivals.
- Visit local horticultural shows.

Task
Design and make a wheelbarrow with one wheel.

Other information
- This is essentially a closed activity, for the children will probably have seen such a wheelbarrow and will therefore offer solutions based on this experience.
- Although the wheelbarrow can be made as a working model, it can also be made child-size to carry lightweight objects in the classroom or garden.
- The wheelbarrow was used in China from about AD 100 onwards.

Sackbarrow

Age range
Six to nine.

Group size
Pairs.

What you need
Scraps of wood of different shapes and sizes, pieces of dowel or cane, pieces of card, stout corrugated cardboard, straws, bobbins, screws and nails, wheels or materials to make them, pieces of plastic tubing, florist's wire, string or yarn, adhesive tape, tools.

Starting points
- Talk about how to make work easier.
- Talk about moving around.
- Work in the school garden.
- Talk about Harvest festival.
- Talk about garden festivals.
- Visit local horticultural shows.
- Visit a railway station.
- Visit a DIY centre.

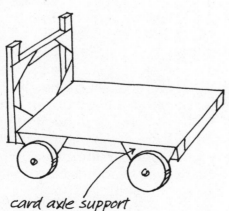

card axle support

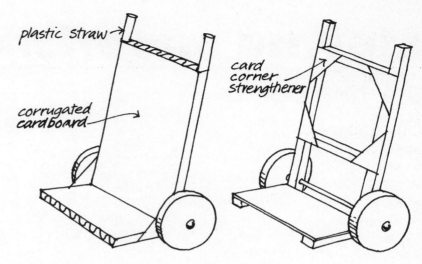

plastic straw

corrugated cardboard

card corner strengthener

Scenario
Have a sack of sand, or potatoes or something obviously heavy and awkward to carry, inconveniently placed, as though left in the classroom by accident.

As the children struggle with it, they will find it difficult to handle and will see the need of a device to move it. Discuss the disadvantages of the wheelbarrow and the advantages of a sackbarrow.

Task
Design and make a sackbarrow to move a sack of potatoes easily.

Other information
- If you are making small-scale models, use a small sack of sand for testing. The sackbarrow, like the wheelbarrow, could be made child-size and used to move lightweight materials.
- Visit a do-it-yourself centre or large garden centre so the children see a variety of styles of trolley and barrow in use. This will give them ideas for linking design to function.

Fork-lift truck

Age range
Seven to eleven.

Group size
Small groups.

What you need
Scraps of wood of different shapes and sizes, pieces of dowel or cane, pieces of card, stout corrugated cardboard, straws, bobbins, screws and nails, wheels or materials to make them, pieces of plastic tubing, florist's wire, string or yarn, adhesive tape, small electric motor, wires and battery, tools.

Starting points
- Talk about how to make work easier.
- Talk about transport.
- Talk about or visit a factory.
- Talk about or visit a building site.
- Observe pallets used for delivering goods eg bricks.

Task
Design and make a fork-lift truck which will lift a weight of about 100g from your desk to a height of 10cm.

Other information
Use a small electric motor with a spindle that is long enough instead of a hand-operated crank.

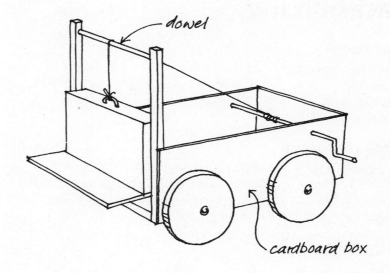

dowel

cardboard box

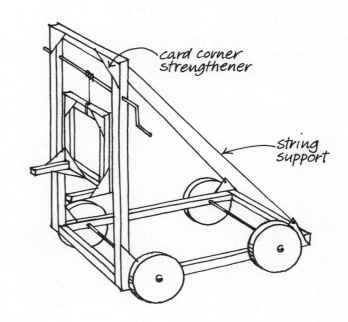

card corner strengthener

string support

Caterpillar-tracked vehicle

Age range
Seven to eleven.

Group size
Pairs or small groups.

What you need
Scraps of wood, card and corrugated cardboard, bobbins, empty metal softdrink cans, screws and nails, small cardboard boxes, assorted plastic trays and containers, pieces of plastic tubing, florist's wire, straws, scraps of dowel or garden cane, string or yarn, adhesive tape, tools.

Starting points
● Introduce a topic on farming and visit a farm.
● Talk about building or construction work.
● Talk about roads and road building.
● Discuss the First and Second World Wars.
● Visit a military museum.

Task
Design and make a vehicle with caterpillar tracks, which runs across a soft surface.

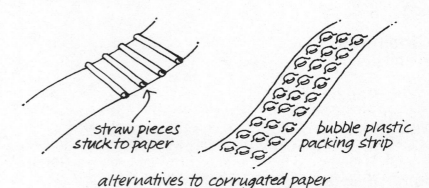

straw pieces stuck to paper

bubble plastic packing strip

alternatives to corrugated paper

Other information
● Test the vehicles by pulling them gently across a tray of soft, damp sand.
● The caterpillar-tracked vehicle was invented by Sir George Cayley in 1825. Cartwheels sank into the muddy roads of the time, and this was his solution.

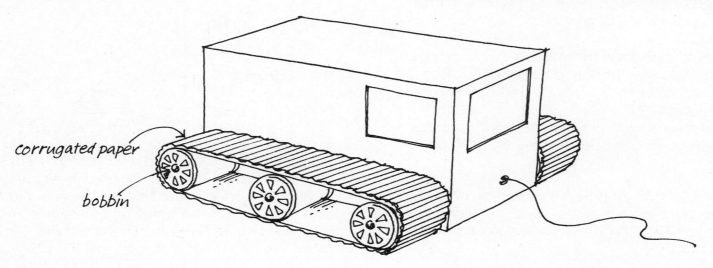

corrugated paper

bobbin

Moonbuggy

Age range
Seven to eleven.

Group size
Small groups.

What you need
Scraps of wood, card and cardboard, bobbins, empty metal softdrink cans, screws and nails, small cardboard boxes, plastic trays and containers, pieces of plastic tubing, sponge balls, florist's wire, straws, elastic bands, dowel or garden cane, string or yarn, adhesive tape, tools.

Starting points
- Discuss the sky and space.
- Talk about landing on the moon.
- Look at the history of transport through the ages.
- Visit a science museum.
- Read *Mr Bowser in the Space Museum* by Philip Curtis (Beaver).

Scenario
Set the scene with a toy truck on which there is a beaker of water. When this is pulled across an uneven surface, there is, inevitably, spillage. Ask the children where they would find surfaces like this. They might suggest poor roads, mountain tracks, even where there are no roads at all. The task can then be presented as a challenge.

Task
This is given as a photocopiable worksheet on page 116. It requires that the children design and make a moonbuggy to cross an uneven surface, carrying its cargo of precious water.

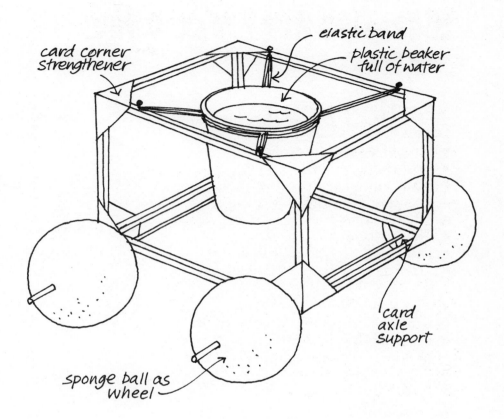

elastic band
card corner strengthener
plastic beaker full of water
card axle support
sponge ball as wheel

Other information
- Assess the solutions by their performance when pulled across three metres of uneven surface. The test surface could be made from pebbles, egg trays or similar bumpy materials.
- They may need to design some kind of suspension harness to avoid spilling the water from the beaker.
- Give each group of children an identical plastic cup, with a standard mark showing the level to which the cup must be filled with water. In the initial trials, it is advisable to use sand, or rice, instead of water.

Smoothing the way

Starting points

Topics
- Structures and forces.
- Bridges.
- Roads through the ages.
- Romans in Britain.
- The age of steam.
- The Victorians.
- Isambard Kingdom Brunel.
- George and Robert Stephenson.

Visits
- Castles and abbeys to look at arches.
- River walk to look at bridges.
- Building or construction site.
- Railway station.
- Railway museum.
- Transport museum.

Stories and rhymes
- *Three Billy Goats Gruff* (traditional).
- *Paddington at the Station* by Michael Bond (Collins).

Events
- Bridge closures in high winds.
- Opening a new bridge.

Smooth roads

Age range
Four to seven.

Group size
Pairs.

What you need
Shallow tray filled with gravel and small pebbles to make an uneven surface, sheet of card, bag of sand, bag of fine gravel, bag of pebbles, toy car, scissors.

Starting points
- Have a project in which you make Roman roads.
- Visit road works near the school.
- Walk along an unmetalled road in bad weather.

Task
Can you make the rough, bumpy road (in the tray) smooth enough for the car to be pulled along?

Other information
- Many roads are built on roads made by the Romans.
- Tarmac (tarmacadam) was first used in 1845 in Nottingham and was a mixture of tar and small stones. With the development of pneumatic tyres, the tarmac surface was not firm enough and so asphalt was used.

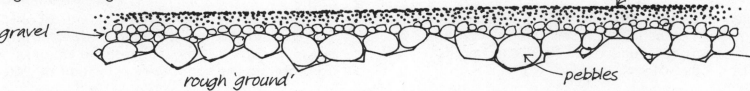

Swamp road

Age range
Six to nine.

Group size
Pairs or small groups.

What you need
Large dish (or cardboard box), polystyrene packing chips, a weight of about 500g, craft matchsticks, pieces of thread about 5cm long, lollipop sticks or half straws, short pieces of garden cane or small twigs.

Starting points
- Look at road building through the ages.
- Look at structures and forces.

Scenario
You are a scientist working in the rainforests of South America, looking for new animals and plants. There has been a terrible rainstorm which has washed away the road back to your camp. To reach safety, you must somehow cross a patch of swamp land. To one side you have high cliffs; to the other, the swamp becomes a dangerous, fast-flowing river. There is no way around the swamp, which may be full of alligators!

You have plenty of natural materials you can use: twigs (matchsticks), branches (lollipop sticks or half straws), logs (garden cane or twigs) and vines (thread).

Task
Using *only* the materials you have been given, design and make some kind of system which will allow you to cross the swamp safely. The solution has to support a weight of 500g in the centre.

Other information
- The dish, or box, can be completely filled with polystyrene packing chips, or similar lightweight material, to represent the swamp. The chips are light enough to move aside or 'flow' when a reasonably heavy weight is placed directly on to them.
- The children are likely to use thread to join the sticks together to make a floating road. An alternative design is to sink piles into the swamp on which to rest the road surface. A suspension bridge is not feasible for there is no access to the other side of the swamp.

Arched bridges

Age range
Seven to eleven.

Group size
Individuals or pairs.

What you need
Four pieces of A4 card, scissors, adhesive and spreader, sheet of newspaper, toy car.

Starting points
- Look at the photocopiable picture of bridges on page 119.
- Look at real bridges.
- Discuss structures and forces.
- Have a project on the Romans and look at their architecture, in particular the semi-circular arch.
- Look at arches in old buildings eg churches.
- Discuss Leonardo da Vinci's work on keystones.
- Read *Leonardo da Vinci* by Alice and Martin Provenson (Hutchinson).

Task
Use the sheet provided on page 117 as a template to cut out and make seven stone shapes from card. Use these card stones to make a bridge which has an arch with a keystone. With the newspaper, make a road over the bridge for a toy car to drive on.

Other information
- The children might need two bricks, or blocks of wood, as supports at the base of the bridge until the final card stone is in place.

A seven 'stone' bridge

- If available, use wooden construction bricks with shaped keystones in addition to the card stones.
- During the fifteenth century Leonardo da Vinci designed and built arches with keystones for buildings and bridges (see *Footsteps into Science*).

Bridges with pillars

Age range
Seven to eleven.

Group size
Individuals or pairs.

What you need
Eight sheets of A3-size newspaper, card, adhesive tape about 10cm long, scissors.

Starting points
- Look at the bridges presented in the photocopiable sheet on page 119.
- Go on an excursion to look at bridges.
- Look at structures and forces.

Task
Using *only* the materials provided, design and make a bridge with supporting pillars to cross a gap, 30cm wide and 20cm deep, which will support a heavy load in the centre.

Other information
- Provide the children with the setting for which they must build their bridge eg on a table, fix shoe boxes 30cm apart.
- Introduce economic considerations by giving the children a fixed budget and inviting them to buy the materials they wish to use.

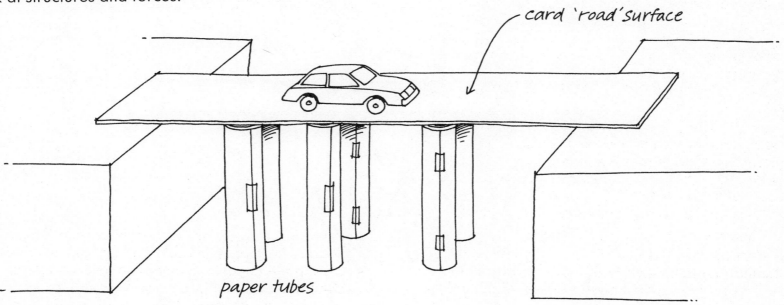

card 'road' surface

paper tubes

Bridges with girders

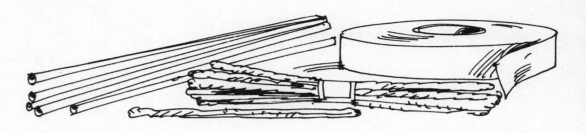

Age range
Seven to eleven.

Group size
Individuals or pairs.

What you need
Twenty straws, five pipe-cleaners, five sheets of newspaper, cut to A4-size, adhesive tape about 10cm long, adhesive and spreader, card for the road surface.

Starting points
- Look at the photocopiable picture of bridges on page 119.
- Look at structures and forces.
- Visit some bridges.

Task
Using *only* the materials provided, design and make a bridge from girders. It must span a gap, 30cm wide and 20cm deep. Test it by lying a card road along its length and pulling a toy car across it.

Other information
- Use the same setting as in the previous activity (Bridges with pillars) to test the solutions.
- Science and mathematics work on strength and shape may be of help to the children.

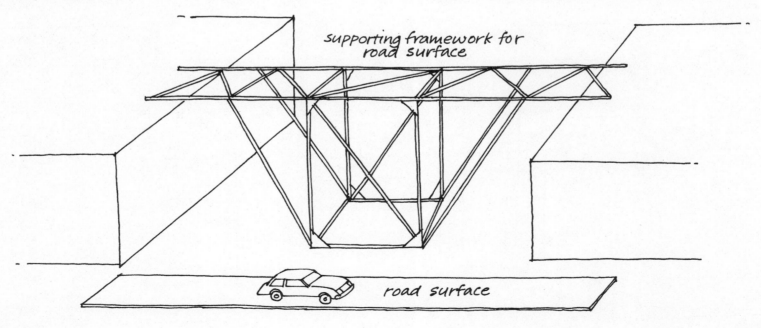

supporting framework for road surface

road surface

78

Suspension bridges

Age range
Seven to eleven.

Group size
Pairs or small groups.

What you need
Twenty straws, five pipe cleaners, five sheets of newspaper, cut to A4-size, adhesive tape about 10cm long, thread about 2m long, small piece of Blu-tak, six lengths of wood about 15cm long and 1cm^2, eight pins, adhesive and spreader, length of card for the road.

Starting points
- Look at the photocopiable picture of bridges on page 119.
- Look at structures and forces.
- Visit a bridge.
- Discuss the work of Isambard Kingdom Brunel.

Task
Using *only* the materials provided, design and make a suspension bridge to span a gap, 30cm wide and 20cm deep. Test it by lying a card road along its length and pulling a toy car over it.

Other information
- Use the same setting as in the previous two activities.
- Introduce economics by giving the groups a fixed budget and asking them to buy their materials.
- Brunel designed and supervised the building of the Clifton suspension bridge. The new Humber suspension bridge has the longest central suspension span in the world, which is some 1,410 metres in length. It is thought that a span of approximately twice this length is possible.

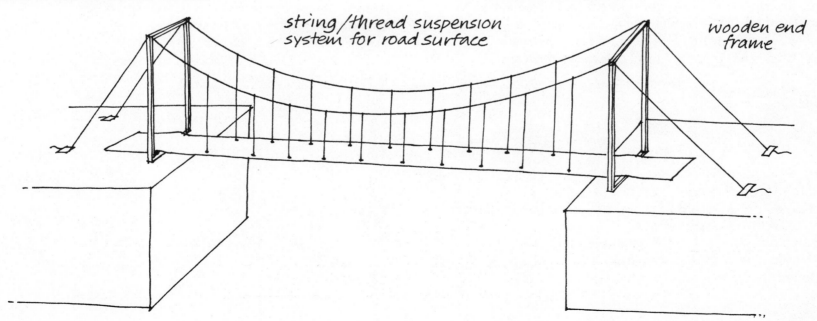

string/thread suspension system for road surface

wooden end frame

Bridge challenge

Age range
Seven to eleven.

Group size
Small groups.

What you need
Straws, pipe cleaners, adhesive tape, thread, A4 sheets of card, adhesive and spreaders, paper clips, paper fasteners, craft matchsticks, scissors.

Starting points
- Discuss and visit some bridges.
- Look at structures and forces.
- Read *Paddy on the Island* by Ursula Moray Williams (Andersen).

Task
The photocopiable worksheet on page 118 sets the scene. The children have to design a bridge to link an island to the mainland. The groups have to work to a budget and have access to purchasable materials.

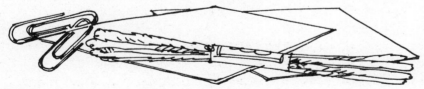

Other information
- The children should have completed the previous activities on different kinds of bridges. They can then draw on those experiences.
- The solutions need to be assessed according to aesthetics, economics and performance.
- You will need five toy cars for testing.

Railway company

Age range
Seven to eleven.

Group size
Whole class, working in small groups.

What you need
Baseboards (made from pieces of blockboard or plywood, each 10cm wide and 20cm long), small boxes, cardboard cut from large boxes, dowel or garden cane, lengths of cross-section wood $1cm^2$, scraps of wood of different shapes and sizes, assorted plastic bottles and containers, string or yarn, adhesive tape, pipe cleaners, paper fasteners, paper clips, drawing pins, screws and nails, adhesive and spreaders, tools.

Starting points
- Have a topic on travel and transport.
- Talk about the age of steam.
- Talk about the Victorians.
- Discuss the work of Robert and George Stephenson.
- Visit a railway station or railway museum.

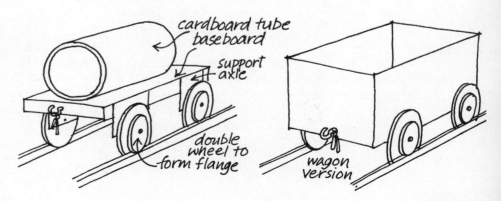

Scenario

Working collectively, the class is going to make a railway system. Initially, each group makes either a truck or carriage to run on railway lines. Link the carriages and trucks together to make a train which can be pulled along the track. Finally, each group should take responsibility for designing and making the buildings and structures found along a railway bank.

Task: first stage

Design and make a truck (or carriage) which can be pulled along the track without coming off the rails. Its base must be made from board, 10cm wide and 20cm long. When completed, decorate the truck. It must have a way of linking on to other trucks and carriages.

carriage version

Other information

- Set up the lines in advance. These can be made from lengths of cross section wood fixed in place with modelling clay. They will need to be about 10cm apart. Place them in a straight path, or, if possible, arrange them to produce a circuit around part of the classroom. Because you have used modelling clay to hold the lines in place, the wood is re-usable when the activity is finished.

Alternatives to cross sections of wood for the tracks are laths, metre rules and pencils. Discuss the fact that the trucks all have to be the same width to run on these tracks. By using standard baseboards you ensure that there is uniformity in the end product.

- For the trucks or carriages to run on the lines, the groups will have to design flanged wheels, with the lip to the inside, or the outside, of the wheel.
- One group will need to make the engine for the train. Make the trucks so that they can be linked to one another.

dowel pieces stuck on to form 'bumper'

'engine'

Task: second stage

Choose, design and make something which is found beside or crossing a railway line. You might make:
- a signal box
- a station platform with buildings
- a bridge over the lines
- a road crossing the lines with gates or barriers
- signals and lights on posts
- a station master's house.

Other information

Let the children make scenery – trees and shrubs, houses, farms and animals – to put alongside the railway system.

Keeping in touch

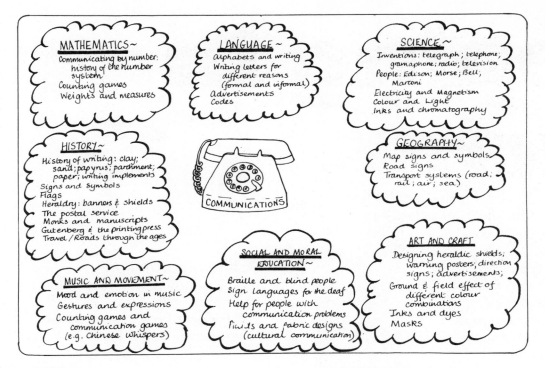

The diagram shows a central "COMMUNICATIONS" topic web with the following branches:

MATHEMATICS~
Communicating by number: history of the number system
Counting games
Weights and measures

LANGUAGE~
Alphabets and writing
Writing letters for different reasons (formal and informal)
Advertisements
Codes

SCIENCE~
Inventions: telegraph; telephone; gramophone; radio; television
People: Edison; Morse; Bell; Marconi
Electricity and Magnetism
Colour and Light
Inks and chromatography

HISTORY~
History of writing: clay; sand; papyrus; parchment; paper; writing implements
Signs and symbols
Flags
Heraldry: banners & shields
The postal service
Monks and manuscripts
Gutenberg & the printing press
Travel / Roads through the ages

GEOGRAPHY~
Map signs and symbols
Road signs
Transport systems (road; rail; air; sea)

MUSIC AND MOVEMENT~
Mood and emotion in music
Gestures and expressions
Counting games and communication games (e.g. Chinese whispers)

SOCIAL AND MORAL EDUCATION~
Braille and blind people
Sign languages for the deaf
Help for people with communication problems
Fluids and fabric designs (cultural communication)

ART AND CRAFT~
Designing heraldic shields; warning posters; direction signs; advertisements;
Ground & field effect of different colour combinations
Inks and dyes
Masks

Getting the message

Starting points

Topics
- Communication.
- The Post Office.
- The history of writing.
- Inventions: telegraph, telephone, radio and television.
- Stamps and stamp collecting.
- Sound.
- Light.
- Satellites and space.

Visits
- A post office.
- A telephone exchange.
- The postman comes to school.

Stories and rhymes
- *Postman Pat* stories by John Cunliffe (Hippo).
- *King Rollo's Letter and other stories* by David McKee (Beaver).

Events
- Letter-writing.
- Christmas post.
- Satellite launch.

Postbox

Age range
Four to seven.

Group size
Pairs or small groups.

What you need
Stout cardboard boxes, card, adhesive tape, string, paper-fasteners, snips, adhesive and spreaders.

Starting points
- Design Christmas cards.
- Write letters, for example to Santa Claus.
- Read the Postman Pat stories.
- Ask a postman to visit the school.
- Set up a post office corner in the classroom.

Task
Design and make a postbox with a flap to keep out the rain and snow.

string hinges for flap

Other information
- You may prefer to make the postbox beforehand, omitting the flap.
- If part of a Christmas theme, a class-produced postbox could be used by all the school.

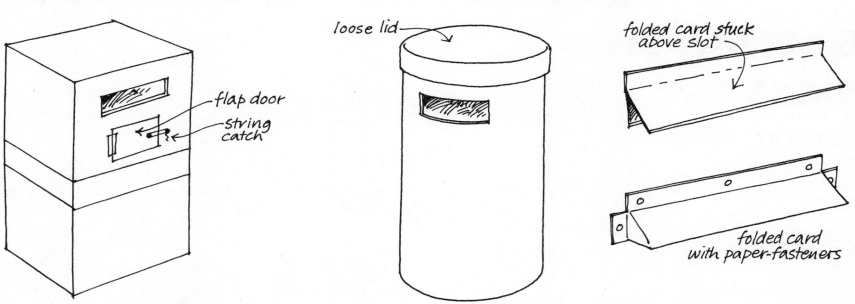

flap door

string catch

loose lid

folded card stuck above slot

folded card with paper-fasteners

84

Parcel balance

Age range
Seven to eleven.

Group size
Small groups.

What you need
Assorted small boxes, card tubes, scraps of wood, dowel or garden cane, assorted plastic tubs and containers, ruler or measuring tape, screws and nails, rubber bands, string or yarn, scraps of sponge, tools, weights eg gram weights, marbles, coins.

Task
Design and make a machine which can be used in a post office to weigh a heavy letter or a small parcel.

Other information
Prepare a heavy letter or small parcel in advance for the children to test their solutions.

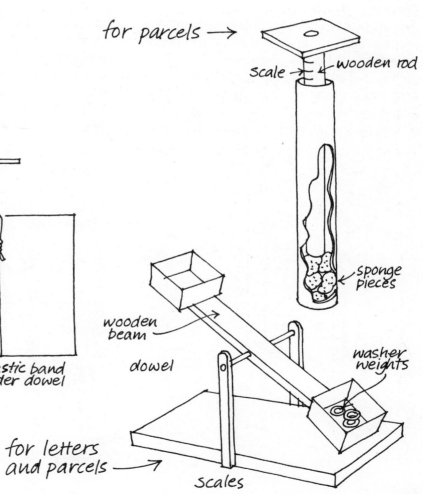

for parcels →

scale →   wooden rod

card top   for letters

scale

dowel

elastic band

tube

elastic band under dowel

wooden beam

dowel

sponge pieces

washer weights

for letters and parcels →

scales

Starting points
- Talk about the Post Office and how it works.
- Plan a project on communication.
- Tell the story of a letter.
- Do work in mathematics on weighing things.

Signals for road and rail

Age range
Six to nine.

Group size
Pairs.

What you need
Scraps of wood of different shapes and sizes, dowel or garden cane, assorted plastic containers, card or cardboard boxes, bobbins, straws, pipe cleaners, coloured acetate film, bulbs and bulbholders, plastic-coated copper wire, 1.5v battery, Blu-tak, adhesive tape, adhesive and spreader, screws and nails, string or yarn, paper-fasteners, paper-clips, drawing pins, tools.

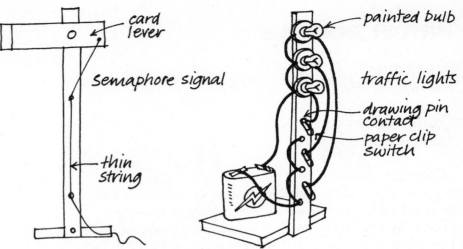

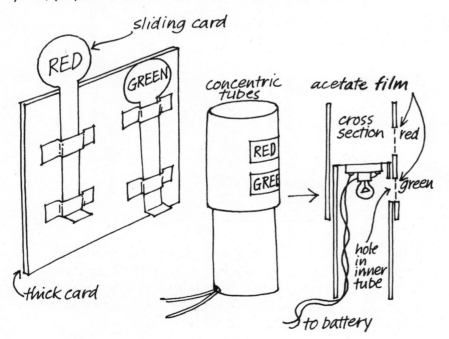

Starting points
- Talk about roadworks.
- Talk about communication.
- Discuss how to make work easier.
- Talk about road safety.
- Describe what the Green Cross Code is about.
- Visit a high street to look at various stop/go devices.
- Read *The Bus Stop* by Nancy Hellen (ABC).

Task
Design and make a stop-go system to use on a road or railway line.

Other information
- The children will probably produce a solution based on simple levers: some might suggest an electrical solution using a battery-controlled light system.
- Link this with 'Taking it easy' (page 44 onwards).
- Traffic signals were first used in the USA in 1914, and they were red and green only. A gas-lamp version was used in London in 1868, but it exploded. Automatic traffic lights were first used in London in 1925.

Lighthouse

Age range
Seven to eleven.

Group size
Pairs or small groups.

What you need
Scraps of wood of different shapes and sizes, small boxes, large cardboard boxes, scissors or snips, adhesive tape, adhesive and spreaders, string or yarn, paper-fasteners, pieces of coloured acetate film, bulbs and bulbholders, plastic-coated copper wire, 1.5v battery, assorted plastic bottles and cups, tools.

Starting points
- Talk about light and energy.
- Talk about lighthouses and lightships.
- Tell the story of Grace Darling.
- Talk about wrecks and wreckers.
- Read *Mr Lively's Lighthouse* by Antonia Feitz (Angus and Robertson) and *Tim to the Lighthouse* by Edward Ardizzone (Oxford University Press).

Task
The task, presented in the photocopiable worksheet on page 122, is to design and build a lighthouse.

Other information
- Assess the solutions on the basis of economics, performance and appearance.
- What was probably the first lighthouse was built by the Greeks on the island of Pharos, near Alexandria during the third century BC. Its light came from a fire.

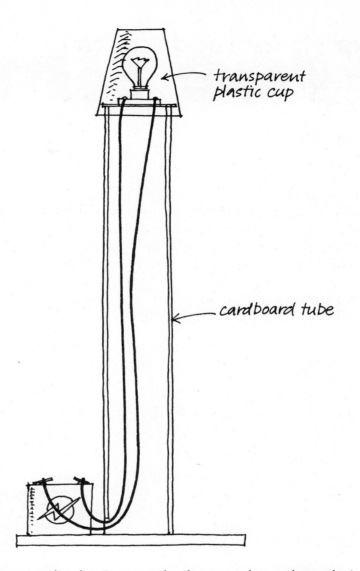

transparent plastic cup

cardboard tube

Subsequently, the Romans built many throughout their empire. The Dungeness Lighthouse of 1862 was the first lighthouse to use an electric lamp. Lighthouses are visible up to twenty miles away, and each has its own pattern of flashes to identify it.

Free time

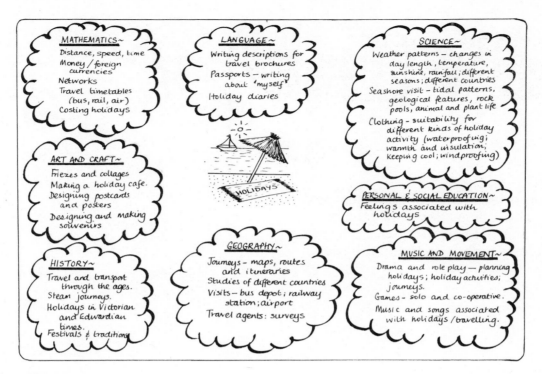

MATHEMATICS~
Distance, speed, time
Money / foreign currencies
Networks
Travel timetables (bus, rail, air)
Costing holidays

LANGUAGE~
Writing descriptions for travel brochures
Passports – writing about 'myself'
Holiday diaries

SCIENCE~
Weather patterns – changes in day length, temperature, sunshine, rainfall; different seasons; different countries
Seashore visit – tidal patterns, geological features, rock pools, animal and plant life
Clothing – suitability for different kinds of holiday activity (waterproofing; warmth and insulation; keeping cool; windproofing)

ART AND CRAFT~
Friezes and collages
Making a holiday cafe.
Designing postcards and posters
Designing and making souvenirs

HOLIDAYS

PERSONAL & SOCIAL EDUCATION~
Feelings associated with holidays

HISTORY~
Travel and transport through the ages.
Steam journeys.
Holidays in Victorian and Edwardian times.
Festivals & traditions

GEOGRAPHY~
Journeys – maps, routes and itineraries
Studies of different countries
Visits – bus depot; railway station; airport
Travel agents: surveys

MUSIC AND MOVEMENT~
Drama and role play – planning holidays; holiday activities; journeys.
Games – solo and co-operative.
Music and songs associated with holidays / travelling.

Town and country

Starting points
Topics
- Castles.
- The Middle Ages.
- Caring, for others and for the environment.
- Birds.
- Weather.
- Pollution.
- Conservation.
- Geology, rocks and soils.

Visits
- Castles.
- Wildlife sanctuary or nature reserve.
- Wildfowl park.
- Reservoir and water-treatment works.

Stories and rhymes
- *Mary Anning's Treasures* by H Bush (Heinemann).
- *Puck of Pook's Hill* by Rudyard Kipling (Puffin).

Events
- Talks with speakers from the Royal Society for the Protection of Birds (RSPB), the Nature Conservancy Council (NCC) and the National Trust.
- Unusual weather conditions.

Castle drawbridge

Age range
Four to seven.

Group size
Small groups.

What you need
Large cardboard box, assorted pieces of card, scraps of wood of different shapes and sizes, dowel or garden cane, string or yarn, bobbins, wheels or the materials to make them, nails and screws, adhesive tape, adhesive and spreaders, paper-fasteners, tools.

Starting points
- Talk about castles.
- Study the Normans.
- Study the Middle Ages.
- Visit a castle with a moat and drawbridge.
- Discuss bridges that open, for example Tower Bridge.
- Talk about ferries and landing craft.

Task
Design and make a castle keep with a drawbridge that can be raised and lowered.

Other information
- Most children are likely to suggest a hand-operated device to raise or lower the drawbridge, but older, or more able, children might use a small, electric motor.
- Design and make a portcullis for the gate to the keep. Show the children an old threepenny piece with a portcullis on it. Let the children consider alternative ways of raising and fixing the portcullis.

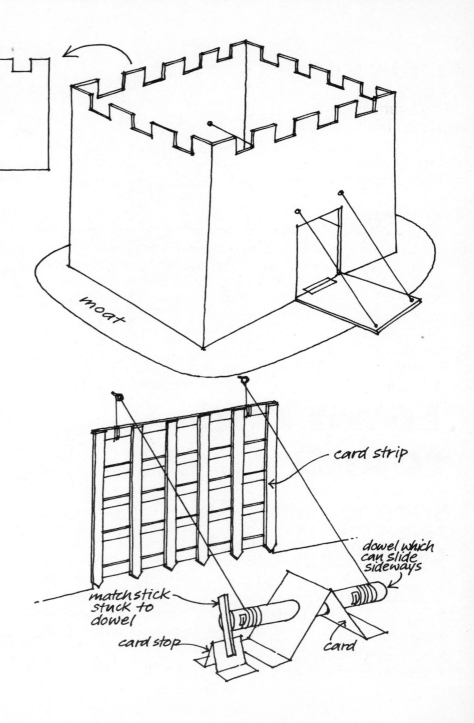

rear view

drawbridge down

up

moat

card strip

dowel which can slide sideways

matchstick stuck to dowel

card stop

card

Bird-table

Age range
Six to nine.

Group size
Pairs or small groups.

What you need
Scraps of wood of different shapes and sizes, dowel or garden cane, pieces of cross-section wood about 1cm^2, string or yarn, florist's wire, corrugated plastic, assorted tin lids, including biscuit tin lids, nails and screws, tools.

Starting points
- Prepare a project on birds.
- Talk about animals in winter.
- Tell the children how to care for living things.
- Arrange a talk by the RSPB (Royal Society for the Protection of Birds).
- Visit a wildfowl park.

Task
Design and make a birdtable for use outdoors to feed the birds in winter.

Other information
- The children might opt for a free-standing structure, but this would require more materials. If resources are limited, restrict the task to a birdtable which can hang from a washing line or the branch of a tree.
- The children need to consider the problem posed by prowling cats. The design should not put birds which are feeding at risk from predators.
- The object should be attractive as well as functional.

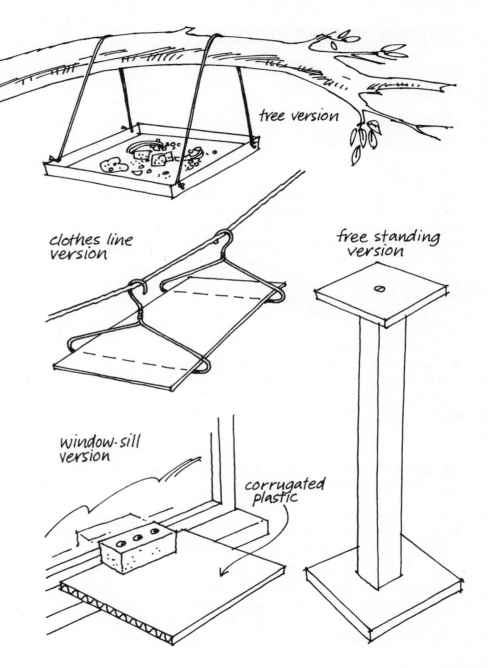

tree version

clothes line version

free standing version

window-sill version

corrugated plastic

Feeding the birds

Age range
Six to nine.

Group size
Pairs or small groups.

What you need
Scraps of wood, assorted plastic bottles and tubs, wire,
string or yarn, craft matchsticks or cocktail sticks,
lollipop sticks, pieces of dowel or garden cane, lids,
tubes, fabric scraps including net, tools.

Starting points
- Prepare a topic on birds.
- Talk about animals in winter.
- Arrange for a talk by the RSPB.
- Visit a wildfowl park.
- Make a bird table.

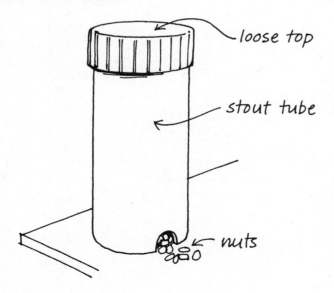

loose top

stout tube

nuts

plastic bottle

nuts

large bottle
lid

Task
Design and make a feeding device to hold peanuts for
the birds in winter.

Other information
- This task should follow the previous activity. The end-
  product can be free-standing or suspended.
- The quality and appearance of the end-product is as
  important as its design and manufacture.
- Extend the activity into an enterprise project by
  selecting a design which can be mass produced and
  sold at an autumn fair.

Windy weather

Age range
Seven to eleven.

Group size
Pairs or small groups.

What you need
Scraps of wood, assorted plastic bottles and tubs, wire, card, plastic tube, string or yarn, craft matchsticks or cocktail sticks, lollipop sticks, pieces of dowel or garden cane, lids, bobbins, fabric scraps, nails, compass, tools.

Starting points
- Start a project on the weather.
- Discuss map reading and orienteering.
- Talk about how the compass works.
- Discuss the concept of moving air.
- Read *The Wonderful Weathercock* by Roy Brown (Edward Arnold).

Scenario
You are on a camping holiday with friends. The weather is fine but windy. You are worried about your tent. Is it in the best position? Will the wind blow it away? What you need is a portable windmeter.

Task
Design and make a portable direction meter for you to gauge the wind direction every day.

Other information
Link the task to geography; the points of the compass and direction, as well as to science; work on weather (National Curriculum, Attainment Targets 9 and 16).

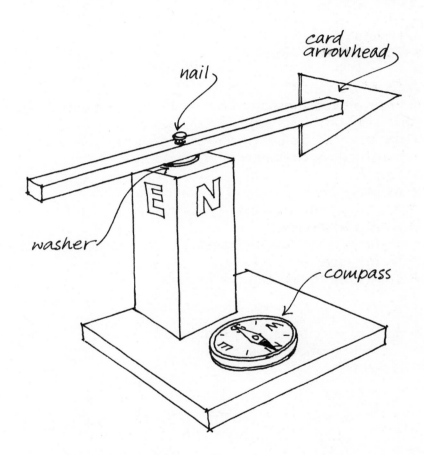

93

Relaxing

Starting points

Topics
- Holidays.
- Fairground.
- Circus.
- Toys.
- Festive occasions.

Visits
- Leisure park or garden.
- Fair.
- Museum of childhood or toy museum.

Stories and rhymes
- *At the Fair* by Helen Herbert (Harcourt Brace Jovanovich).
- *Only One Toy* by Smadar Samson (ABC).

Events
- Special occasions, for example a birthday.
- Collection of old toys.
- Holidays.

Moving toys

Age range
Six to nine.

Group size
Individuals.

What you need
Thick card, paper-fasteners, strong thread or thin string, adhesive and spreaders, adhesive tape, stout scissors or snips, hole punch.

Starting points
- Visit a toy museum.
- Collect old toys.
- Collect toys for a charity.
- Talk about how things move.
- Read stories and rhymes: *Peter Pan; Humpty Dumpty; Only One Toy* by Smadar Samson (ABC).

Task
The activity is described for the children on two photocopiable worksheets, pages 120, 121. It is in two distinct parts, involving the making of a card figure with a moveable part.

Other information
- The task extends the children's experience of simple levers and pivots.
- Having made a crocodile and/or Humpty Dumpty, ask the children to choose a character from a story, or rhyme, and to design and make it for themselves.

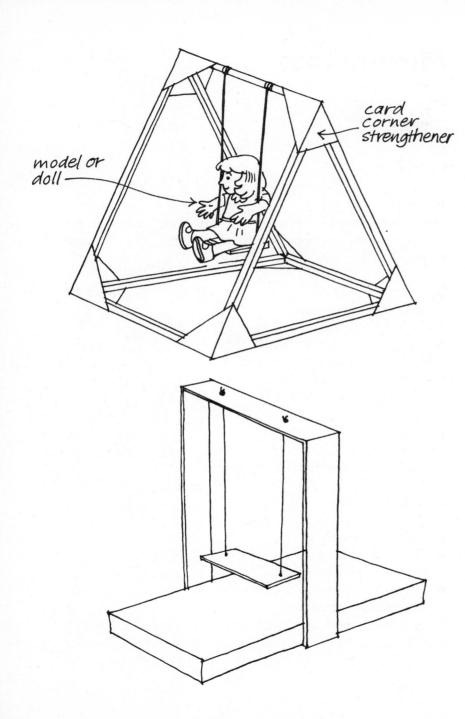

card corner strengthener

model or doll

Swing

Age range
Four to seven.

Group size
Pairs or small groups.

What you need
Scraps of wood of different shapes and sizes, stout cardboard boxes, florist's wire, string or yarn, card, adhesive and spreaders, adhesive tape, tools.

Starting points
- Visit a children's playground.
- Visit a leisure park.
- Collect pictures of a child's swing.
- Talk about the work of a circus trapeze artist.
- Read *Adventure Playground* by Helen Burgess (Hodder and Stoughton).

Task
Design and make a free-standing swing on which a small figure can sit.

Other information
Extend the task by asking groups of children to make different playground equipment, for example a slide and a see-saw. Collect them together to form a model children's playground.

Fairground roundabout

Age range
Seven to eleven.

Group size
Small groups.

What you need
Scraps of wood, dowel or garden cane, plastic lids, trays and containers, paper plates, bobbins, string or yarn, adhesive and spreaders, card, straws, small electric motor, plastic-coated copper wires, battery, tools.

Starting points
- Visit a fair or collect pictures of a fair.
- Observe 'the witch's hat' roundabout in playgrounds.
- Talk about things which go round.
- Read *Carousel* by B Wildsmith (Oxford University Press).
- Refer to the photocopiable sheet on page 123.

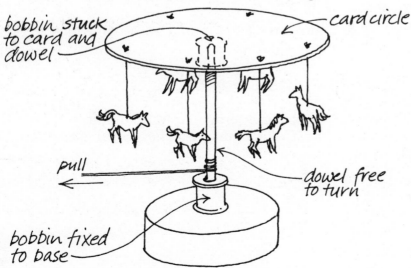

Task
Design and make a roundabout which spins. Decorate it.

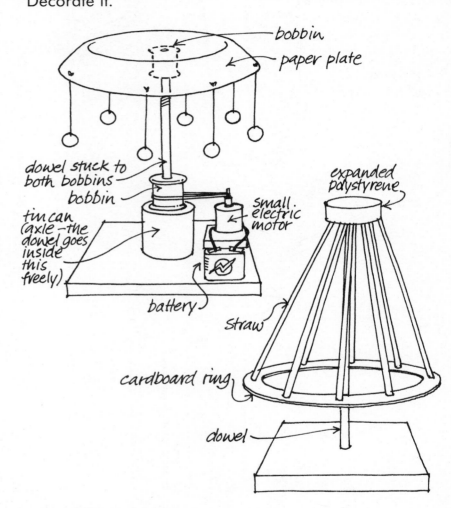

Other information
This task is related to the following one, the helter-skelter. Extend the activities to build a model fairground. Include swing boats, dodgems and side shows.

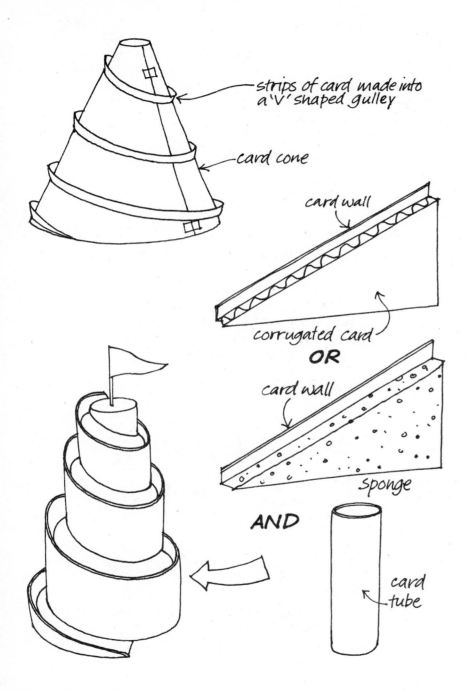

strips of card made into a 'V' shaped gulley

card cone

card wall

corrugated card

OR

card wall

sponge

AND

card tube

Fairground helter-skelter

Age range
Seven to eleven.

Group size
Small groups.

What you need
Scraps of wood of different shapes and sizes, cardboard from large boxes, assorted plastic trays and containers, string or yarn, adhesive and spreaders, adhesive tape, card, sponge, straws, tools.

Starting points
- Visit a fair or look at pictures of a fair.
- Look at pictures of a children's slide.
- Look at the slide at the swimming baths.
- Look at what makes work easier: inclines and ramps.
- Discuss the history of roads: Roman roads curved over obstacles; Saxon roads spiralled around them.
- Collect devices that use inclines eg screws, drill bits.
- Refer to the photocopiable sheet, page 123.

Task
Design and make a helter-skelter which will allow a marble to roll from the top of the ramp all the way down to the bottom.

Other information
- This is a relatively closed problem, intended to show that helter-skelters and similar structures are 'wrapped up' inclines.
- Precede the work by making a screw. Do this by wrapping a right-angled triangle of card around a toilet-roll tube.

Pop-up cards

Age range
Four to eleven.

Group size
Individuals.

What you need
Card, adhesive and spreaders, adhesive tape, scissors or snips, paper-fasteners.

Starting points
- Discuss the festive occasions when cards are sent.
- Talk about birthdays.

Task
Design and make a card with a pop-up figure.

window through to disc

rotating disc

paper-fastener

Other information
- The simplest solution is the slit and the sliding card. However, children who have made Humpty Dumpty or the crocodile (page 94) might decide to use a lever and pivot action.
- With younger, or less able, children have a ready-made pop-up card to show them to stimulate ideas.

Happy Easter

pop-up picture

Music time

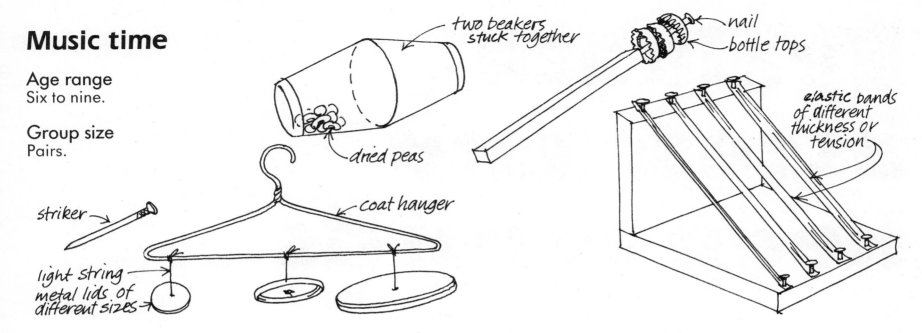

Age range
Six to nine.

Group size
Pairs.

two beakers
stuck together

dried peas

nail
bottle tops

elastic bands
of different
thickness or
tension

striker

coat hanger

light string
metal lids of
different sizes

What you need
Scraps of wood, empty tins and cans, plastic tubs, plastic and metal lids, elastic bands, nails and screws of different sizes, coat-hangers, string or yarn, tools.

Starting points
● Listen to sound and music.
● Talk about music at a funfair.
● Listen to music from different countries.

Task
Design and make an instrument which can be used in a class band.

Other information
● Let the children compare the instruments they have made with those available in school.
● Display a set of unusual instruments such as wind chimes.

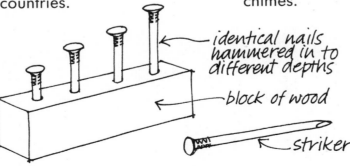

identical nails
hammered in to
different depths

block of wood

striker

Evaluate, assess and keep records

As design and technology is a part of the National Curriculum, formal assessment of children's attainment will be partly through DES Standard Assessment Tasks. However, you will also need to carry out your own assessment during each key stage. Assessment is as much a reflection of teacher-provision as of pupil-performance, so it must:

- *evaluate* what has been planned for the children, why and by what means;
- *assess* what each child has done;
- *record* the performance of each child in an appropriate way.

Evaluate

The nature of design and technology makes evaluation easier to plan for than some other areas of the curriculum. This is because a task or activity can be selected and presented to the *whole* class, yet groups and/or individuals can perform at their own level within the task framework. From the point of view of planning – what the children are going to do and why – you can think of the class as a whole, rather than plan separate tasks. This is not to say that tasks cannot be developed exclusively for individuals or small groups. At times, there will be both the need and the opportunity for this.

Planning makes progression possible in children's all-round development. You will need to plan progression in:
- physical development: manipulative skills, gross and fine motor control, use of tools.
- intellectual development: application of knowledge and understanding, the use of thinking skills and strategies, working with creativity and imagination.
- social and emotional development: personal qualities, appropriate attitudes.

It is unlikely that you can incorporate all these aspects in a single activity, so it is important to keep continuous planning records of the experiences. From these records, a picture of progression develops.

DESIGN & TECHNOLOGY ACTIVITY RECORD

Class:_____ Teacher:_____ Date(s):_____
Activity:_____

Products:	Experiences of concepts, facts, ideas.....
◆ Materials & Components	
◆ Structures	
◆ Forces	
◆ Energy	
◆ Movement	
◆ Control	
◆ Mechanisms	
◆ Systems	

Processes:	Personal, Social and Intellectual Skills used
◆ Exploring & Investigating ~ to find needs and problems	
◆ Imaging & Generating ~ ideas for solutions	
◆ Modelling & Researching ~ producing a design brief	
◆ Organising & Planning ~ most appropriate solution	
◆ Making & Testing the solution	
◆ Appraising ~ the solution	
◆ Using Tools & Equipment ~ appropriately, safely, accurately	

People:	Social and Cultural aspects and constraints
◆ Business & Economics	
◆ Aesthetics	
◆ Health, Safety & Responsibility	
◆ Social & Environmental needs	
◆ Historical & Cultural Aspects	

Figure 1

DESIGN & TECHNOLOGY ACTIVITY RECORD

Class: PRIMARY 3 **Teacher:** Ms Jones **Date(s):** Term 2, Week 3

Activity: Potato Carrier: Designing & Making paper bag with limited materials

Products:	Experiences of concepts, facts, ideas.....
• Materials & Components	Investigating strength of different types of paper
• Structures	Preliminary work on structures (tubes, cones etc.)
• Forces	Pulling & twisting forces; gravity; weight
• Energy	—
• Movement	—
• Control	—
• Mechanisms	—
• Systems	—

Processes:	Personal, Social and Intellectual skills used
• Exploring & Investigating ~ to find needs and problems	Linked to need to solve problem (carry the potatoes)
• Imaging & Generating ~ ideas for solutions	Thinking of own solutions based on limited resources
• Modelling & Researching ~ producing a design brief	
• Organising & Planning ~ most appropriate solution	Dividing task between them and carrying it out; fair testing of bags using potatoes
• Making & Testing the solution	
• Appraising ~ the solution	aesthetics as well as function
• Using Tools & Equipment ~ appropriately, safely, accurately	Scissors; accuracy of measurement; fixing techniques

People:	Social and Cultural aspects and constraints
• Business & Economics	Working with limited materials
• Aesthetics	Decorating bag to make it attractive
• Health, Safety & Responsibility	Danger of suffocation from plastic bags
• Social & Environmental needs	Need for bags weighed against litter and waste of resources
• Historical & Cultural Aspects	Margaret Knight & the satchel bottom bag.

Figure 2

A record sheet, based on the National Curriculum document recommendations, is given in Figure 1. Fill it in for each experience completed by the children (whether as a class, in groups, or individuals).

The left-hand column lists the broad areas of products (to gain knowledge and understanding), processes (to acquire skills) and people (to understand social, cultural and historical aspects). The right-hand column is for you to list the specific opportunities offered through each activity. Not all blocks will be filled for each activity because the aims and objectives of a given task will tend to focus on particular objectives. For example, if the brief was to design and make a carrier-bag using limited materials (see page 34), the boxes likely to be completed are those shown in Figure 2.

Assess

Next you will need to assess progress made. Unlike planning, this has to be done for each child. Since children will tend to work in groups rather than as individuals, this may not be easy. Finding opportunities to observe a group for a reasonable length of time may be a problem.

Although children may be involved in design and technology tasks every week, it is not necessary (or feasible) to assess everything they do. It may be practical to assess each group only once per term.

It may be tempting to leave assessment until the last week of term, but it is better if the load is spread, for example by observing one group per fortnight.

The second problem likely to occur is that of assessing each child's individual contribution. Because of its practical nature, and because sharing ideas and working together are important for design and technology, it is often necessary to observe the children working co-operatively, but it is equally important to identify individual progress and development. For the National Curriculum, the assessment criteria are based on the Attainment Targets. This gives a sequence of stages through which the children can progress in the application of skills, knowledge and understanding. The context in which they work can also bring in social, cultural and historical aspects.

Record keeping

Since most of the design and technology in the primary school is likely to be within the framework of broader projects, systematic record-keeping is essential.

It is a simple matter to make a note on the Activity Record Sheet that that particular activity was used as an assessment task with a particular group of pupils.

It is a more complex matter to record progress in a clear, succinct manner. Given that Design and Technology is only one of many areas of the curriculum requiring continuous monitoring, you need a recording system which is as brief as possible, easy to complete and can be interpreted at a glance.

Our suggestion for this is the Recording Wheel, shown on page 106.

The wheel has been designed to reflect the Attainment Targets and Profile Components of the National Curriculum for Technology. The five Attainment Targets are drawn as five equal segments of the wheel. The five Levels of Attainment considered appropriate for the primary school (that is, Key Stage 1 – Levels 1 to 3 and Key Stage 2 – Levels 2 to 5 inclusive) are shown as concentric circles. Within each level the separate statements of attainment are identified.

Figure 3

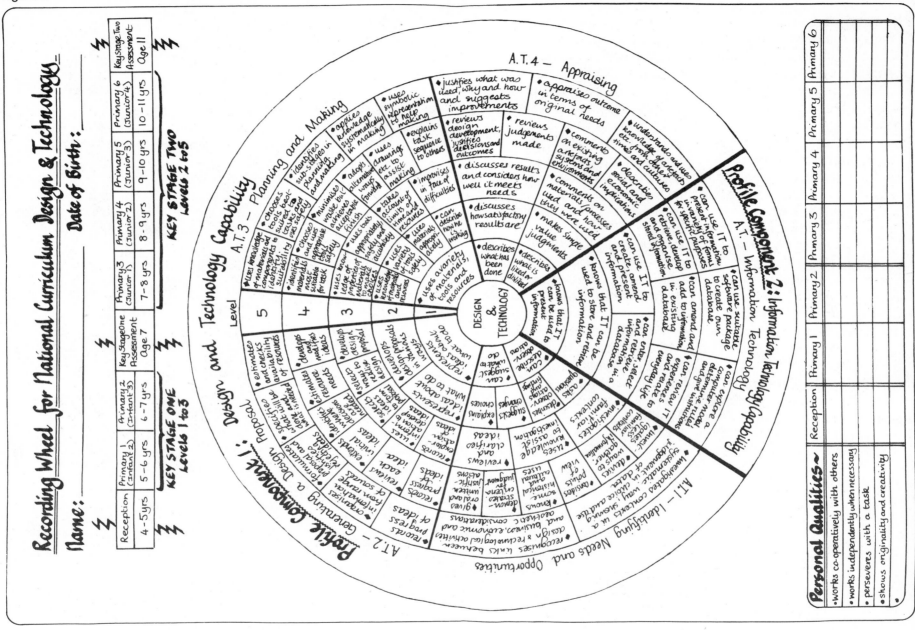

Since assessment of Design and Technology will be focusing on the whole activity, it is unlikely that each attainment target will be taught as a self-contained unit. Rather, there will be a spread across many of the statements of attainment within a particular narrow range of levels. You can mark on the wheel the levels of attainment successfully achieved after observing the children in their tasks. Make the record more visual by allocating a particular colour to each class, perhaps the colours of the rainbow through the school.

One of the strengths of this concentric approach is that it is easy to see where gaps are developing and to correct them. Weaknesses in a child's development can be seen early and remedial action can be taken.

The recording wheel allows you to have a clear picture of each child's progress as it relates to the National Curriculum. It allows comparisons to be made at moderation meetings, and it is a useful aid in discussing a child's progress with parents.

Reproducible material

Design and technology train, see page 7

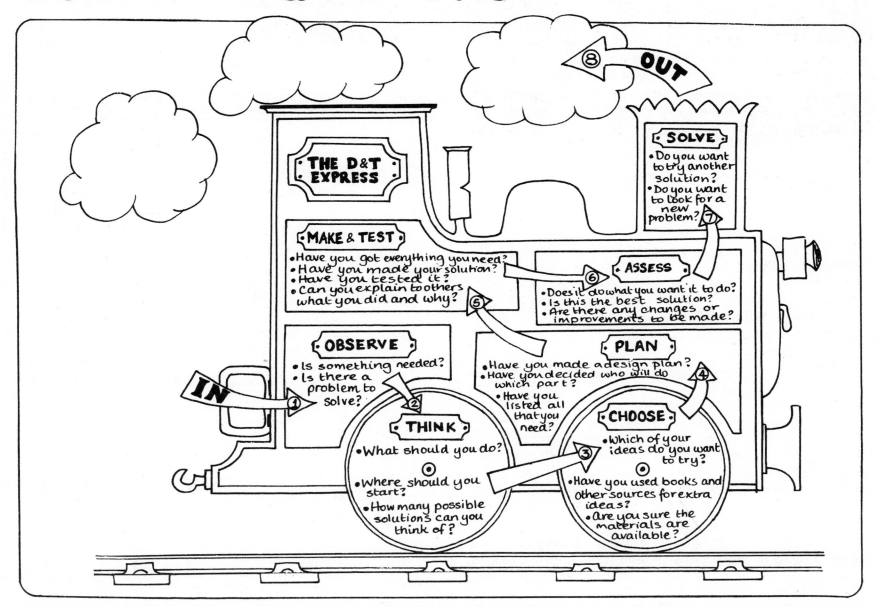

Build a two-storey house, see page 20

Imagine that you and your family are moving to a different part of the country. There are no houses for sale so you must design and build one yourself. It must have two floors (an upstairs as well as a downstairs) and a sloping roof. It must also have a back door and a front door and some windows. Anything else you wish to include is up to you.

You have £100 in the bank. You can spend up to but no more than this amount.

You can buy the items you need from your local Do-It-Yourself centre. They cost:

large box	£25
small box	£10
sheet of thick card	£8
sheet of thin card	£5
sheet of polythene	£3
decorating materials	£3
card tube...	£2
fabric pieces	£1
adhesive tape	£1 per 10cm
string	£1 per 5cm
straws..	£1 each
paper-fasteners	£1 for five

Work with one or two friends. First you must design your house. What will it look like from the front? From the back? How many windows will it have? What is the roof like? Next, calculate how much you will spend on the items you will need to build it.

Once you are happy with your design and you can afford to build it, buy what you need and begin building.

Decorate the outside of the house to make it attractive.

Wishing well, see page 37

Today we take it for granted that when we turn on the tap we will get pure, clean water to drink. People in some countries are not so lucky. In the past this was not the case in this country either. People had to collect water in other ways. One way was to use a well. You can still see wells in very old villages or in the grounds of large buildings like castles. Make a model well.

What you need
A piece of carpet tube, cardboard, cross-section wood, about 1cm^2, wire, glue and glue spreaders, thread, plastic tub, bottle top.

What to do
- Cut a piece of carpet tube to a length of about 10cm. Stand the plastic tub inside it.
- Cut two pieces of wood, each 20cm long. Drill a small hole through each piece of wood, 5cm from one end.

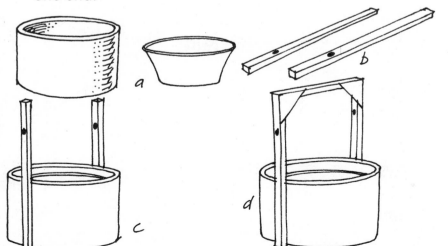

- Stick the two pieces of wood to the tube, opposite one another, with the small holes uppermost.
- Measure the distance across the top of the two pieces of wood. Cut a third piece of wood to fit across the top. Stick it into place. Stick card triangles across the corners to strengthen the joints.
- Cut a piece of wire to a length of about 20cm. Push it through the two holes in the wood. Using pliers, bend about one centimetre of one end of the piece of wire so that it cannot slip back through the hole. Bend the other end to make a handle. This is the winding mechanism for your well. Tape some thread on to the centre of the bar and wind up the thread.
- Make a bucket from a bottle top.
- Make a roof for your well. Decorate it.

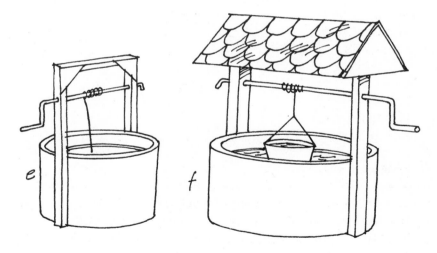

Follow-up
- From one sheet of A4-size newspaper, make a bucket for your well which will hold water.
- Make a brake for the well so that the bucket does not fall when not in use.

Grain mover, see page 49

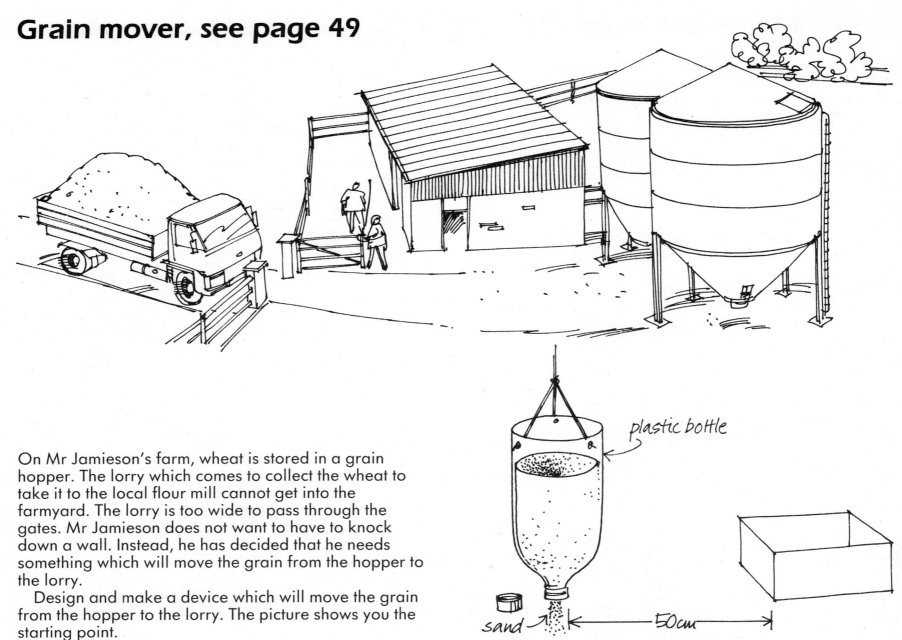

plastic bottle

sand

50 cm

On Mr Jamieson's farm, wheat is stored in a grain hopper. The lorry which comes to collect the wheat to take it to the local flour mill cannot get into the farmyard. The lorry is too wide to pass through the gates. Mr Jamieson does not want to have to knock down a wall. Instead, he has decided that he needs something which will move the grain from the hopper to the lorry.

Design and make a device which will move the grain from the hopper to the lorry. The picture shows you the starting point.

Jumping frogs, see page 52

Colour the frog green.
Carefully cut him out.
Fold the piece of card in half.
Stick the frog on to the piece of card.
Make sure that the frog's eyes are on the folded edge of the card.
Your frog should look like this:

Use adhesive tape to fix an elastic band to the inside of the card.
The picture shows you how.

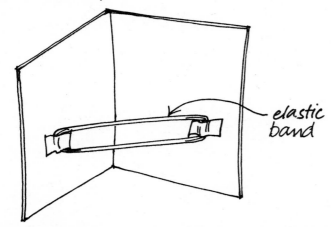

elastic band

Press down on the folded card and let go.
Does your frog jump?

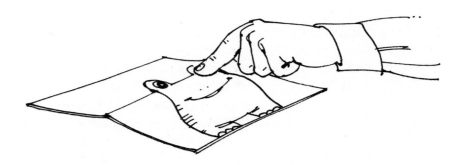

Problem
- Can you make an animal which will jump out of a box to give your friends a fright?
- How will you make it jump when the box is opened?
- Try it.

The pull of gravity, see page 54

What you need
A piece of dowel or rod, string, yoghurt pot full of sand or marbles, bobbin, matchbox full of modelling clay.

Task
Investigate how the speed with which the matchbox falls depends upon how much sand is in the tub. How can you make the matchbox move up and down very slowly and steadily?

Problem
Design and make a lift to work in a cardboard box.

What you need
A large cardboard box, string, matchbox filled with modelling clay, bobbin, dowel, garden cane or old pencils, card, adhesive tape, scraps of wood.

Task
Mark two floors on your cardboard box. You will need to cut out two sets of lift doors. Can you make your lift move up and down between the two floors? Can you think of a way to stop it from going too far up or down?

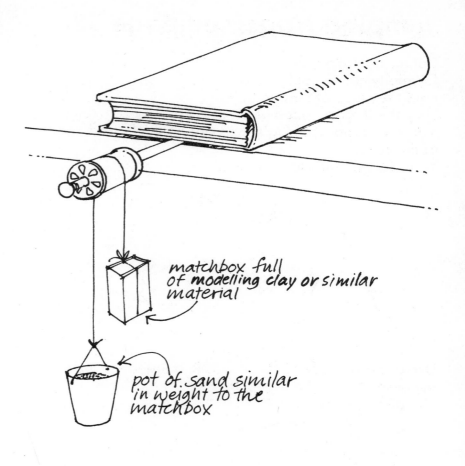

matchbox full of modelling clay or similar material

pot of sand similar in weight to the matchbox

Self-propelled vehicle, see page 68

Imagine you hope to work for a large Japanese car manufacturer. You have been asked to design and build a powered vehicle which will travel a great distance under its own power. It must be made as cheaply as possible. The manufacturer will then assess all your designs for cost, appearance and performance and, on the basis of that information, decide who will be offered the job.

You can buy the following materials:

wood ....50p per piece
plastic containers .... 25p each
1cm^2 cross-section wood 50p
   for one piece, 25cm long
card..20p sheet
adhesive and spreaders............................25p pot
dowel or garden cane.............. 50p for one piece,
   25cm long
wheels .... 10p each
thread or string.......... 5p for one piece, 10cm long
small cardboard box................................. 50p each
small electric motor.................................. 50p each
wires (for circuits)................................... 10p each
battery.. 20p each
elastic bands... 2p each
modelling clay .... 2p piece
plastic propeller .... 10p each
balloons... 5p each

Other materials might be available from your supplier, but you need to agree prices with the store manager.

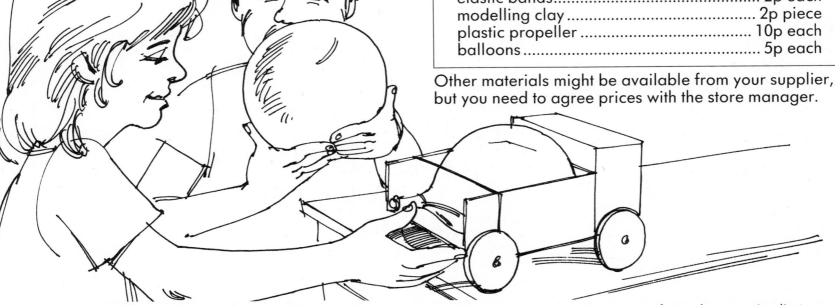

Moonbuggy, see page 73

You are a space technologist working on the 'Moonbase project'. You have been asked to design and build a moonbuggy which will move across the bumpy surface of the moon. It must carry a tank of much needed water to the base on the dark side of the moon. Since there is no water on the moon, it must be brought in by spaceship. It is therefore very important that none of the water is spilled.

You will need to produce a design brief for assessment by moonbase controller, showing the development of your team's ideas and the final design.

Once this has been approved by the controller, you must collect the materials and build the buggy.

It will be tested on the moonbase testbed, which the Controller has had especially built.

Arched bridges, see page 76

You need building bricks to make your arched bridge. You can make these from card with the help of the template here. Cut out the template. Draw around it. Cut out the shape you have just drawn. Carefully make firm folds on the lines which say FOLD HERE. Put adhesive on the patch which says STICK HERE. Press the patch on to the opposite side and hold it until it sticks firmly. Do this again until you have made seven building bricks.

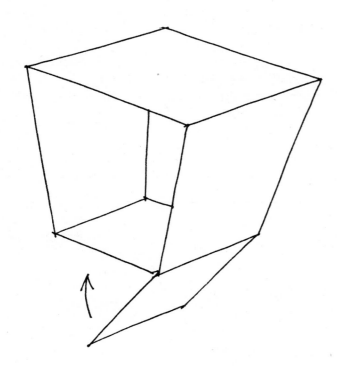

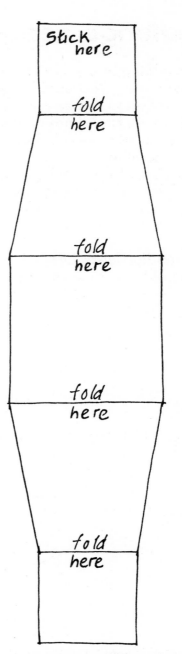

stick here

fold here

fold here

fold here

fold here

Bridge challenge, see page 80

A storm has destroyed the bridge which links the island of Abonda to the mainland. The island council has asked you and your team to design and build a new bridge. The people of the island are not very rich. They gave you £50 to spend on materials. Remember that you cannot spend more than this.

First, you must submit your design plan to the council for approval. Your plan must take into account the cost of the materials.

If the council agrees to it, you may go ahead and buy your materials.

When you have made your bridge, any *whole* items which you have bought but not used may be sold back to the shop.

The materials cost:

straws	£1 each
paper clips	£1 each
paper fasteners	£1 each
craft matchsticks	£1 each
pipe cleaners	£2 each
adhesive tape	£1 per cm
thread	£1 per cm
newspaper	£3 per A4 sheet
card	£5 per A4 sheet
adhesive and spreader	£1 per pot

When finished, your bridge must be able to carry simultaneously the weight of five toy cars.

The distance from the mainland to the island is 50 cm. The sea is 50 cm deep.

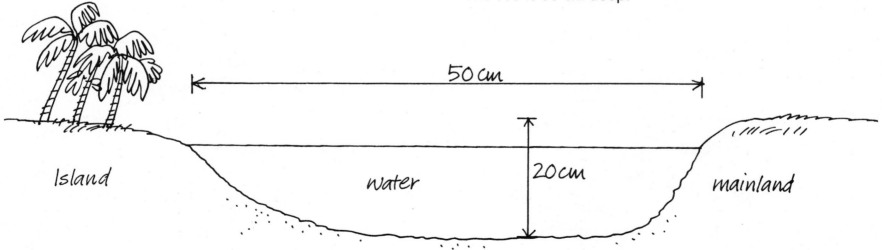

50 cm

20 cm

Island

water

mainland

Bridges, see pages 76 to 80

Moving toys, see page 94

CROCODILE

What you need
A sheet of card, scissors, adhesive and spreader, paper-fastener, crayons.

What to do
- Colour the crocodile pieces opposite and then cut them out.
- Stick them carefully on to your piece of card.
- Cut out the two pieces of the crocodile.
- Carefully make a hole through each crococile piece where there is a big dot. You might need to ask someone to help you to do this.
- Push the paper-fastener through the piece that has the eye. Then push it through the piece with the tail. Open the paper-fastener so that the two pieces stay together.
- Move the tail up and down, and your hungry crocodile will open and close its mouth.

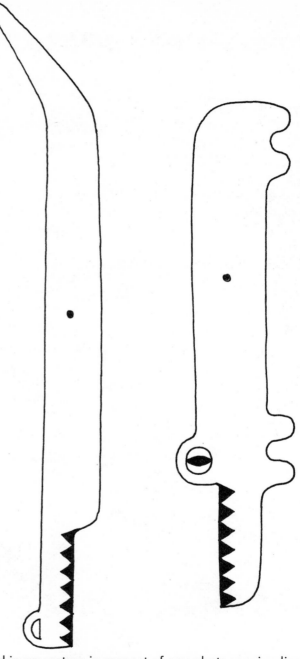

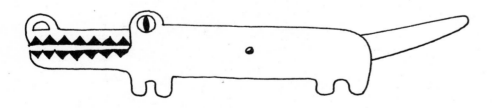

Moving toys, see page 94

HUMPTY DUMPTY

What you need
A sheet of card, scissors, adhesive and spreader, paper-fasteners, strong thread or string, crayons.

What to do
- Colour the different parts of Humpty Dumpty and then carefully cut each one out.
- Stick them onto the piece of card. Make sure that they hold.
- Carefully cut out the nine pieces of Humpty Dumpty.
- Make a hole through each piece of Humpty Dumpty where there is a big dot. You might need to ask someone to help you to do this.
- Push a paper-fastener through each of the four holes on Humpty Dumpty's body. Next, push the paper-fasteners through the two arm pieces without hands and the two leg pieces without feet.
- Use paper-fasteners to join the hands and the feet in the correct places.
- Finally, fix the thread to the back of Humpty Dumpty. When you pull the thread, Humpty Dumpty will dance.

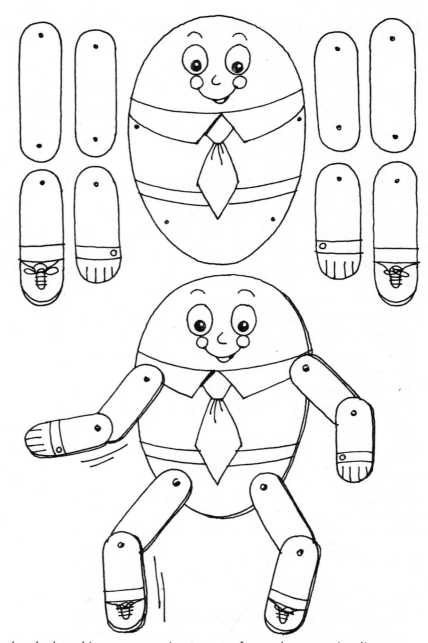

Lighthouse, see page 87

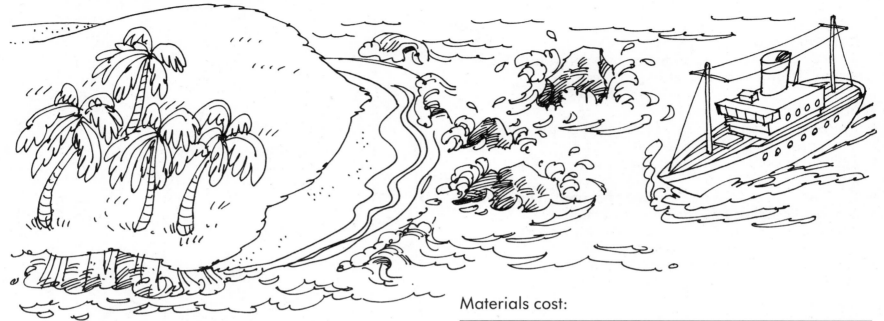

There are lots of dangerous rocks to the north of the island of Abonda. The local people keep away from them, but sometimes ships are wrecked there during foggy or stormy weather. The council has decided that it wishes to build a lighthouse so that there will be no more wrecks.

You have been asked to produce a design for a lighthouse and, if the council approves it, you are to build it. The people of the island are not rich, so you must not spend more than £40 on the lighthouse.

With your team, produce a design and present it to the council for approval. If the council approves it go ahead and build your lighthouse.

Your lighthouse will be judged by the island council according to how well it works *and* what it looks like.

Materials cost:

scraps of wood	£1 piece
small boxes	£10 each
large boxes	£25 each
adhesive tape	£1 for 10cm
adhesive and spreaders	£1 pot
string or yarn	£4 for 20cm
paper-fasteners	£1 for 5
piece of coloured acetate	£1 per piece
bulb and bulbholder	£5 per set
plastic-coated copper wire	£2 per piece
1.5v battery	£10 each
plastic bottle	£10 each

You may sell back to your supplier any leftover whole materials.

Fairground, see pages 96 and 97

Resources

Using construction kits

Using construction kits is an important way of helping young children to gain experience in handling materials and modular components. They can see matching modules, like wooden bricks, being used to make totally different shapes. With the more complex kits, they can make working models and moving structures. The use of kits should be built into the planned programme for design and technology, keeping in mind that:

- there should be as wide a variety of kits as possible;
- the kits should not be the property of one class but should be available to all;
- you should plan how to introduce the children to new kits as they are bought;
- within the classroom, the kits should be used across the curriculum whenever possible, especially in science and mathematics;
- the kits need to be securely stored yet easily accessible to the children;
- the kits need to be maintained and supplemented to avoid the frustration of missing pieces.

Try local jumble sales to supplement your kits, or ask if older children could pass on unwanted kits from home.

Start with
Free play: children become familiar with the bits and pieces and learn how to fit them together in different ways.

Progress to
Copying: children use pictures that you have supplied or those provided on workcards in some commercially produced kits to copy the ideas and translate two-dimensional ideas into three-dimensional objects.

Eventually
Creating: Children use their own ideas to construct. Initially they may need a stimulus from you – a suggestion as to what to make, or build, or a picture to generate ideas, but later they will develop their own ideas.

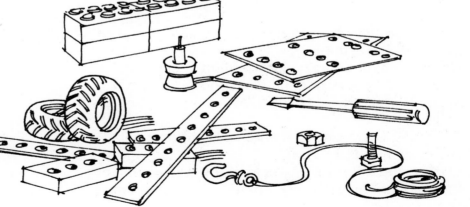

Kits suitable for Design and Technology include; Briomec, Capsela, Construct-o-straw, Construx, Duplo, Fischer Technik, Geo-struct, LEGO, Ludoval, Meccano, Mobilo, Quadro, Stickle bricks, LEGO-Technic, Teko, Tyco super blocks, Tyco robo-blox, wooden building blocks.

Suppliers

These will provide catalogues or information sheets on request.

E J Arnold & Sons Ltd, Parkside Lane, Dewsbury Road, Leeds LS11 5TD.
Griffin and George Ltd, Meadow Road, Loughborough, Leicestershire LE11 0RG.
Hestair Hope Ltd, St Philip's Drive, Royton, Oldham, Lancashire OL2 6AG.
Nottingham Educational Supplies Ltd, 17 Ludlow Hill Road, West Bridgeford, Nottingham NG2 6HD.
Osmiroid International, Osmiroid Works, Fareham Road, Gosport, Hampshire PO13 0AL.
Porters of Selby Ltd, Station Road, Selby, Yorkshire YO8 0NP.
A & L Scientific, Unit 14A Progress Industrial Park, Orders Lane, Kirkham, near Preston, Lancashire PR4 2TZ.

These also provide information or catalogues useful for Information Technology.
Department of Industry, Information Technology Division, 29 Bressenden Place, London SW1 5D7.
Rickitt's Educational Media, Ilton, Ilminster, Somerset TA19 9BR.
Tecmedia Ltd, 5 Granby Street, Loughborough, Leicestershire LE11 3DU.
Contact the Information Technology Advisor in your local education authority. Some LEAs have computer centres, which are accessible to teachers.

Try local stores and DIY centres; the selection of equipment is often greater and at sale times prices can be lower than those of standard suppliers.

Reading

Aitken, J & Mills, G, *First Steps in Technology*, Holmes McDougall.
British Association for the Advancement of Science, *Ideas for Egg Races and Other Problem Solving Activities*, BAAS.
Avon Local Education Authority, *An Approach Through Problem Solving*, Primary Science Working Paper 3, County of Avon Primary Science and Technology Centre.
Department of Education and Science, *Design and Technology for Ages 5–16*, HMSO.
Fisher, R, *Problem Solving in Primary Schools*, Basil Blackwell.
Johnsey, R, *Problem Solving in School Science*, Macdonald.
Meredith, M & Briggs, B, *Big Trak Plus*, Council for Educational Technology.
Newton, D P, *Making Science Education Relevant*, Kogan Page.
Newton, D P & Newton, L D, *Footsteps into Science*, Stanley Thornes.
Stewart, J, *Exploring Primary Science and Technology with Microcomputers*, (MEP Readers No 5), Council for Educational Technology on behalf of the Microelectronics Education Programme.
Williams, P & Jinks, D, *Design and Technology 5–12*, Falmer Press.

Tools and equipment

Each working group should have its own box of tools. Plastic storage boxes, available from most DIY centres, are useful. For each group, the box should include, if possible, the following tools and equipment.

Measuring and marking: compasses, metal ruler, felt-tipped pens, pencil.

Cutting to size and shape: bench hook, hand drill, junior hacksaw, spare hacksaw blades, craft knife, drill bits, snips or stout scissors.

Joining and fixing: assorted nails, claw hammer (heavy), nail punch, pin hammer (light), screwdrivers (plain and cross-head), assorted screws, adhesive spreaders or lollipop sticks, PVA adhesive (in small pot with lid).

Smoothing and shaping: files (assorted shapes), sandpaper.

In addition, some tools may be required only occasionally, and so you may need only one of these in the class. These include: coping saw, cross-cut saw, adhesive gun (plus spare glue sticks), hand drill mounted on stand, leather hole punch, long-armed stapler, tenon saw.

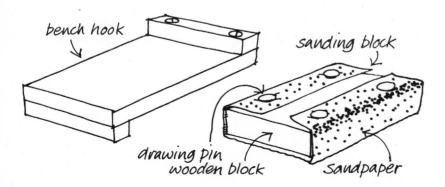

bench hook

sanding block

drawing pin wooden block

sandpaper

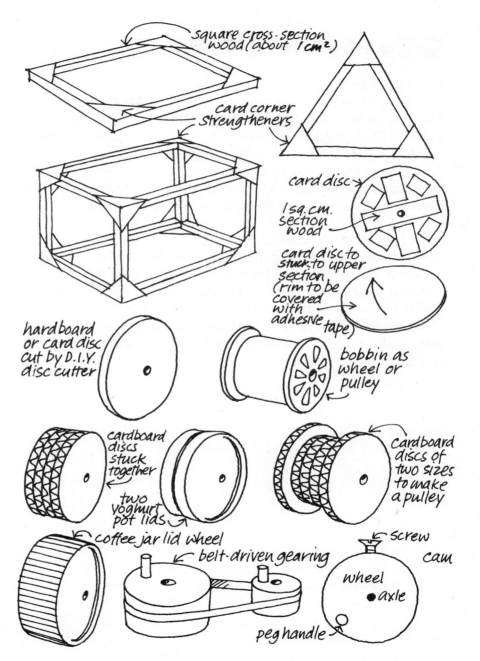

square cross-section wood (about 1 cm²)

card corner strengtheners

card disc

1 sq. cm. section wood

card disc to stuck to upper section (rim to be covered with adhesive tape)

hardboard or card disc cut by D.I.Y. disc cutter

bobbin as wheel or pulley

cardboard discs stuck together

two yoghurt pot lids

cardboard discs of two sizes to make a pulley

coffee jar lid wheel

belt-driven gearing

peg handle

screw

cam

wheel

axle

Other Scholastic books

Bright Ideas
The Bright Ideas books provide a wealth of resources for busy primary school teachers. There are now more than 20 titles published, providing clearly explained and illustrated ideas on topics ranging from *Spelling* and *Maths Games* to *World of Work* and *Using Books in the Classroom*. Each book contains material which can be photocopied for use in the classroom.

Teacher Handbooks
The Teacher Handbooks give an overview of the latest research in primary education, and show how it can be put into practice in the classroom. Covering all the core areas of the curriculum, the *Teacher Handbooks* are indispensable to the new teacher as a source of information and useful to the experienced teacher as a quick reference guide.

Management Books
The Management Books are designed to help teachers to organise their time, classroom and teaching more efficiently. The books deal with topical issues, such as *Parents and Schools* and organising and planning *Project Teaching*, and are written by authors with lots of practical advice and experiences to share.

Let's Investigate
Let's Investigate is an exciting range of photocopiable activity books giving open-ended investigative tasks. Designed to cover the six to twelve-year-old age range, these books are ideal for small group or individual work. Each book presents progressively more difficult concepts and many of the activities can be adapted for use throughout the primary school. Detailed teacher's notes outlining the objectives of each photocopiable sheet and suggesting follow-up activities have been included.